394

W9-AAF-779

THE NEW
BOOK OF DAYS

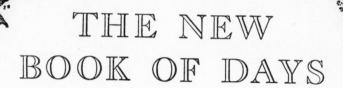

THE NEW
BOOK OF DAYS

By

Eleanor Farjeon

Illustrated by

Philip Gough and M. W. Hawes

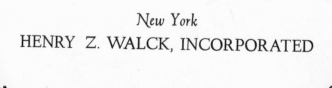

New York

HENRY Z. WALCK, INCORPORATED

First published, London, 1941
First American edition, 1961
Library of Congress Catalog Card Number: 61-8583

PRINTED IN THE UNITED STATES OF AMERICA

FOREWORD

A MOMENT of interest may create a lifetime of curiosity. It is one of the valuable qualities; it is the impulse to go and find out for oneself; a really curious person will keep his eyes and wits open for anything connected with what has aroused his interest.

I don't pretend in this Book of Days to have provided 366 such moments for everybody who looks into it. I may, if I'm lucky, have provided twenty for this one, a dozen for that one, and a couple for another. A personality, an incident, a description may be the match that will light a candle and illumine a room for somebody. A rhyme, a tradition, an oddity may be a finger-post to a little unsuspected journey off the beaten track. I hope that almost anybody will find one track diverting enough to be followed to its end. Some of the tracks—like Shakespeare—are highways that he is bound to discover for himself one day; some, like Giraldis Cambrensis, are by-ways he may chance upon, some time or other; and there are queer little footpaths he might never find at all, such as the Olde, Olde, Very Olde Man.

This old man was a fact. Every instance in this book springs out of some fact, in history or legend, some truth in the real or the imaginary world (for truth resides in both of them). I have often avoided obvious events, persons, and ceremonies which mark a special date, in favour of something less known. My choice has fallen where it pleased me most. If it tempts any of you to look further into Cobbett's *American Journal*,

[5]

or White's *Selborne*, or Miss Fanny Kemble's delightful New York Diaries, or Miss Fanny Burney's earlier and much more delightful Diaries, or Will Kempe's *Nine Daies Wonder*, or the letters of John Keats, or Nansen's *Farthest North*, or one of a hundred other books which will bring you to a thousand others: then you will find that my speck of gold has discovered to you a gold-mine. But I have not tried to tell a lot, or explain a lot. Explanations are for lesson-books, and this isn't a lesson-book. Nor is it an anthology of pieces from other authors. The quotation marks are not entirely lacking, but generally I have retold the things I have found. The verses are mine, and so are the proverb tales, though not, of course, the proverbs they illustrate. I now wish that I had stated the proverb itself in every instance, and in case they are not easily enough found inside the story, here they are in their order:

From China: *You cannot stop the birds of sorrow from flying through your hair, but you need not let them nest there.*

From Italy: *Do yourself a kindness, sir, said the beggar.*

From Russia: *Every man loves the tree that gives him shelter.*

From Russia: *If you are a cock, crow; if you are a hen, lay eggs.*

From Scotland: *Naebody's sweetheart's ugly.*

From Serbia: *Marry by the ear, not by the eye.*

From Russia: *We are brothers, the same sun has dried our rags.*

From Belgium: *The empty ear of corn holds its head the highest.*

From England: *So sure as you've an orchard somebody brings you apples.*

From Russia: *The fall of a leaf is a whisper to the living.*

From Italy: *It is the common soldier's blood that makes the general great.*

From Serbia: *Give to a child, but promise him nothing.*

For the roots of the word-meanings with which I have played about I have to thank Mr. G. C. Earle, whose knowledge of words has not only roots but wings. A word, says another Russian proverb, is a bird which once let fly can never be recalled. If any child flies away on the back of one of mine, he will only be following the example of Homer and Mother Goose, who had so much in common. For they both spoke to the people in 'winged words'.

I have followed as nearly as I could the dates on which certain festivals fall in 1941, when the New Year falls on a Wednesday. One date has played me false. 'Summertime' should fall in April. After the book was written, too late for changes, this capricious date slipped back, in 1940, into February, and a cold and misty morning that first day of Summertime was. What and when it will be in 1941, who can say? And what does it matter? For Time is but 'a nothing and a joke', and this New Book of Days itself will one day be old.

HAMPSTEAD,
February, 1940.

[7]

JANUARY

First Things and Frost

FEBRUARY
Saints and Superstitions

[9]

MARCH

Blowing and Growing

APRIL
Fools and Fooling

MAY
Flowers and Songs

JUNE
Sunshine and Gold

JULY
Dreaming and Drowsing

[14]

AUGUST
Sea-Sands and Corn

[15]

SEPTEMBER
Orchards and Harvests

OCTOBER
Farewells and Falling Leaf

B

[17]

NOVEMBER
Fire and Smoke

DECEMBER
Feasts and Fairies

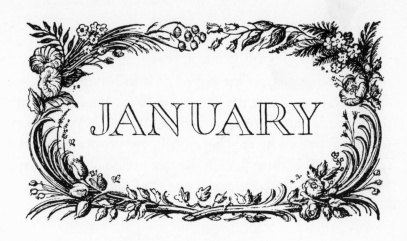

JANUARY

JANUARY 1

Song of the Very Poor
(*From the Old French*)

OLD Year is out.
  Laugh and make merry!
When you have your heart's desire,
Turn about,
Remember the very
                    Poor
Who have no food or fire.

New Year is in.
Eat and be merry!
After you have drunk and fed,
Then begin
To think of the very
                    Poor
Who want for meat and bread.

JANUARY 2

Ringwood Bread

THERE is a place in the New Forest in Hampshire where
nobody need sing the Song of the Very Poor on January
the Second. For this day nobody in Ringwood need want
for bread; free loaves are given to all poor persons who come
for them. For three hundred years and more, this day's
bread has been the poor man's right in Ringwood.

JANUARY 3

New Year's Gift

IN one of Ben Jonson's old masques you will find this stage
direction:

Enter New Year's Gift!

And a very gay fellow was he. He came on the scene
'in a blue coat, serving-man like, with an orange, and a
sprig of rosemary on his head, his hat full of brooches, with
a collar of gingerbread, his torch-bearer carrying a marchpane, with a bottle of wine on either arm'.

Marchpane was a cake of marzipan, and part of the New
Year's feast. Rosemary was for remembrance of past years.
And he carried an orange because, in Ben Jonson's day, one
of the favourite New Year's gifts was an orange stuck with
cloves. Ben himself was January-born, in 1574, when the
streets were not as sweet-smelling as they might be; so you
carried a clove-orange to sniff at now and again.

JANUARY 4

JACOB GRIMM *was born* 1785

Grimm and the Little Girl

JAKOB was the elder of the two Brothers Grimm, who collected fairy-tales from everywhere for everybody.

They were also very learned professors, with simple hearts.

One day, when Jakob was living in Göttingen, a little girl tripped to his door, and knocked.

'What do you want?' asked the maid who opened the door.

'I want to see the Herr Doktor,' said the child.

When she was shown into Jakob Grimm's study—

'And did *you* write all those fairy-tales?' she asked.

'Yes, my child.'

'The one about the clever little tailor, too?—and you said at the end whoever does not believe it must give you a Thaler?'

'Yes, my child.'

'Well then, I don't believe it!' said the little girl, and she laid down a Groschen on the learned Doctor's desk.

'What is this for?' asked Jakob Grimm.

'It is on account,' said the little girl. 'I haven't a whole Thaler now, so I shall have to pay you a Groschen at a time.'

JANUARY 5

The Luck of the Cake

IN a Herefordshire wainhouse, as Westcountry-folk call the place where the oxen are stalled, an old ox and a young one stand side by side.

YOUNG BOSS: There's goings-on out there.

OLD BOSS: Yes to be sure. 'Tis Twelfth-Day Eve, the Wassail. The Master and his men are lighting the thirteen fires in the wheatfield.

YOUNG BOSS: What for?

OLD BOSS: For custom's sake, to make sure of fortunate crops. Twelve little fires and one big fire must be kindled on Twelfth-Day Eve, and old cider drunk in a ring around the flames. Hearken to 'em halloo!

YOUNG BOSS: I seem to hear all Herefordshire hallooing.

OLD BOSS: Yes, boy, farm answers to farm from the thirteen fires in the wheatfield.

YOUNG BOSS: I wish I might see some of the doings.

OLD BOSS: Patience. Our part is to come.

> *Presently to the wainhouse comes the* BAILIFF, *who is head of the ox-herd, and after him the* MASTER *with a great cup of ale, and the* MISTRESS *with a big cake baked in a ring, and behind them their friends and servants.*

OLD BOSS: Watch, boy. Now all of us yokefellows will be toasted, and he that is toasted first is held to be the pick of the bunch.

> *The* MASTER *lifts the ale-cup, cries 'Young Boss!' and drinks. How the young one's heart swells as the Wassailers shout his*

[24]

*name. Then each ox is toasted in turn, and hailed by the
drinkers; and last, the* BAILIFF *cries: 'Now, Missus, let us see
who takes the cake.' 'Fair dealing!' laughs the* MISTRESS, *and
gives the cake to the* MASTER, *who hangs it on* YOUNG BOSS'S
*horn, and tickles him suddenly in a tender place. Taken un-
aware, the young ox tosses his head, the cake spins backward,
falls behind his tail, and—'The luck of the cake is mine!' cries
the merry* MISTRESS. *'Now, maids and men, to the kitchen!
We'll never let Twelfth-Day morning catch us sleeping!' And
so the Wassailers go dancing out of the wainhouse.*

YOUNG BOSS: But why did the Mistress take the cake?

OLD BOSS: Because you tossed it backward over your tail. If
you had tossed it forward into the boosy, the Bailiff would
have had the luck of the cake for the coming year.

YOUNG BOSS: The ways of men are curious.

OLD BOSS: And of women.

JANUARY 6

The First Lamb

SHEPHERD, good shepherd, the wind's blowing cold.
What are you doing out there in the fold?
   I hark for a sweet
   And whimpering bleat,
A lamb has been eaned, friend, upon the south wold.

Shepherd, good shepherd, come in from the wet,
The New Year has risen, the Old Year has set.
   Bring the first lamb
   To the fire with her dam,
Though bitter the time be, she'll ean her lambs yet.

JANUARY 7
St. Distaff's Day

'QUAH-QUAH!' said the Old Grey Goose to her Goslings, 'St. Distaff's they may call it if they *like*, but there never *was* a St. Distaff that *I* know of, this was just a joking name men gave to the Seventh Day of the year, because when the Twelve Days of Christmas were done, work must begin again, women must spin again, come what may, toil after play, that's always the way, so on this day the women of the world took up their distaffs and span a fine thread, clothes for the children and sheets for the bed, though spinning is not what it was when *I* was a gosling, for believe it or not a young lady of Norwich span a pound of combed wool so exceedingly fine that when it was finished it stretched in a line of one-hundred-and-sixty-eight thousand yards, which is close upon one hundred miles long, and *that* is no nursery fable or song, my goslings,' said the Old Grey Goose, 'for I've seen it in print with my own two eyes, quah-quah!' (*And so have I.*)

JANUARY 8

Everyday Word-Meanings: NEIGHBOUR

HAVE you ever thought about the simple words you speak every day? Words have grown up in the English language as flowers grow up in an English field. But the roots of the flowers have often come out of fields in other countries: the French field, the German field, the Latin field, the Greek field, have all planted some of their roots in our English field, and they have settled there, and flowered into English words. The best of our words grow from roots out of the Anglo-Saxon field. Anglo-Saxon was the early language of England, it is the mother tongue, and many of the words we speak to-day are its children.

Here's a simple word we may use any day: *Neighbour.*

No matter where you live, you will have a neighbour. The word was born in the time when the Anglo-Saxon peasant, or boor, tilled the soil; and the boor who lived nearest to him on the land became his Nigh-Boor. So wherever your home may be, somebody else's home will be nearest to it; and he will be your neighbour, and you, of course, will be his.

Perhaps your neighbour will live on the same landing as you do, or over your ceiling, or under your floor—that is, your neighbour's home may be in the very house you live in. If you live in a semi-detached house, you may still hear your neighbour singing, or hammering, or quarrelling, through the wall. If your house is a detached house, your neighbour's will be the next house in the street, only a few feet away. If your cottage stands by itself in the country, your neighbour may be fifty yards away. If you live on a ranch in South America, your neighbour may be fifty miles away. The word has taken on a wide meaning, and your neighbour, as long as he is next you, need no longer be nigh you, nor need he be a boor.

For boor itself has changed its meaning for us. Like a peasant who leaves his village to come into town, a word may travel from the country-side to the cities; and the city may give the word, as well as the peasant, a new life, not always for the better. The boor who tilled the soil had his peasant-wits about him; but when he came among the sharper-witted townsfolk, they considered him a dull lout compared with themselves. Then the word 'boor' ceased to have its good honest meaning, and became the way of describing anybody with clumsy manners and stupid wits.

We no longer call our English farmers boors; but the Dutch ones are still Boers, dull farmers and clever ones. And we can be pretty sure that those early English tillers of the soil were not all stupid, but had the natural wisdom which comes to most people who have the earth and the sky for their Nigh-Boors.

JANUARY 9

January's Song

I DRIVE boys out
With blithesome shout
On frozen pond
To make their din;
From barren wood
In search of food,
My silver wand
Drives Robin in.
Lo! lo! in by-ways cold
Aconite shows his penny of gold.
Baa! baa! the first lamb bleats,
And nuzzles at the old ewe's teats.

JANUARY 10
Buffalo Bill
(*Died* 1917)

WHEN William Frederick Cody was born in Iowa, on 26 February 1845, there were no railways across Western America. Relays of ponies carried the mails over prairie and mountain, from St. Joseph to Sacramento; and the riders in the Pony Express had to face such dangers as Indians, buffalo, desperadoes, and prairie fires.

Bill Cody could ride anything, shoot anything, rope anything; he was riding for the Pony Express in his 'teens, and scouted for Abraham Lincoln in the American Civil War. By the time he was twenty he was known as Colonel Cody.

After the War, railways across the Wild West began; the ponies lost their jobs, and thousands of men found theirs. Men need meat. To provision the workers was a problem. Colonel Bill Cody undertook to provide the railwaymen on the prairie with buffalo-steaks. In eighteen months he killed 4,820 buffalo, and became known for life as Buffalo Bill.

He looked round for the next adventure; as none was forthcoming, he decided to relive the past, and turn his exciting life into a world-circus. Cowboys and Cowgirls, Indians and Squaws, Ponies and Buffalo, were all a part of 'Buffalo Bill's Wild West Show'. It caught like wildfire all over America; and crossing the water didn't damp it down. It caught like wildfire in all the capitals of Europe.

Colonel Bill Cody lived to see the beginning, but not the end, of the Great War. He died in Denver, Colorado, on 10 January 1917.

J321 FLATLANDS AVE. & EAST 100 ST. BROOKLYN, N. Y. PUBLIC SCHOOL 242

JANUARY 11

The Duke of Norfolk's Party

ON the 11th of January 1664 young Mr. Browne of
Norwich put on his grandest suit to attend the birthday
party of his friend Henry Howard. It was likely to be a party
out of the common, for Henry's father was the Duke of
Norfolk. Mr. Browne's father also had a title of his own;
Sir Thomas Browne was given to writing religious medita-
tions, but his son was fonder of dancing.

The day after the party, young Mr. Browne called at his
Aunt Bendish's, where he frequently dined; and his aunt
must needs hear all about the party—'for,' said she, 'we had
enough dull days under Oliver Cromwell; why, Noll even
forbade us our maypole on Mayday and our plumb-pudding
at Christmas. But times are bettered since the Merry

Monarch came back, so now let's hear all the extravagances you can remember, nephew.'

'Well, aunt,' said the young man, 'there was more than maypoles and plumb-puddings, I assure you! Henry had spared no expense. To fetch our fair partners from a distance, he had three huge coaches—the greatest cost no less than £500, and carried no fewer than fourteen young ladies. We danced in a great room built for the purpose, and you never saw such rich hangings as covered the walls! Then, at table, we ate out of pure gold banquet, though I confess the candles and snuffers were of silver, but so were the fire-shovels and tongs. We ate to the tunes of the best musicians of Norwich, and after the feast, when the Duke's gates were thrown open, so many people flocked in that Henry had the beer set out in the street, hoping it would keep some of the crowd there. Even as it was, we had scarce knee-and-elbow room to dance in; yet we kept it up till the watchman called Two-O'clock-and-a-Frosty-Morning.'

'Bless me!' said Aunt Bendish. 'If the man in the moon himself came down to Norwich, he couldn't tell us greater wonders than this.'

JANUARY 12
Charles Perrault
(Born 1628)

*A*ND *who, please, was Charles Perrault?*

Good gracious, Child! (*said the Old Lady*) You ought to be ashamed of yourself! Charles Perrault was a Frenchman, a Scholar, a Critic, a Lawyer, and an honoured Member of the French Academy of Letters.

But I don't care if he was, ma'am.

Don't you indeed! (*sniffed the Old Lady*) Then let me tell you, Charles Perrault not only took the trouble to write your fairy stories for you, when he was seventy years old, but he created the most famous Nursery Character of 'em all.

Do you mean Alice, ma'am?

No, I do *not* mean Alice! (*snapped the Old Lady*) Alice was created by another Charles, for all he chose to change his name to Carroll, and he was a mere youngster to *my* Charles, who created immortal creatures two and a half centuries ago.

What immortal creatures did Charles Perrault create, ma'am?

Bluebeard, Tom Thumb, and Puss-in-Boots, to be sure!

But none of these is famouser than Alice, ma'am.

Who said they were, Child? Nevertheless (*smirked the Old Lady*), Charles Perrault created one famouser than all the rest of 'em put together.

Who was it, if you please, ma'am?

Mother Goose (*said the Old Lady. And flew out of the window*).

Charles Perrault

BORN 1628

Philip Gough

JANUARY 13
Plow-Monday
(*The First Monday after Twelfth-Night*)

TURN out for Plow-Monday!
Up, fellows, now!
Buckle the horses
And follow the plough.
Guide the share truly
And slice the square sods,
Wave upon wave of them,
Where the horse plods.
Then the land, ready
And turned, looks its best,
Even more hopeful
Than when it is dressed
Green with the corn-blades
And crop-leaves of May,
Red with the wheat-sheaf
And gold with the hay.
God bless all fellows
Who buckle to now,
Spending their Plow-Monday
Speeding the plough.

JANUARY 14
The Great Frost
(*St. Hilary's Day*)

MUFFLE up well for St. Hilary! the coldest day in the year. Perhaps it is called so because, in 1205, such a frost began on the 14th of January as England has not known before or since. The Great Frost held, says an old chronicle, 'till the two and twentieth day of March, so that the ground could not be tilled; whereof it came to pass that, in summer following, a quarter of wheat was sold for a mark of silver, which for the more part in the days of King Henry the Second was sold for twelve pence; a quarter of beans or peas for half a mark; a quarter of oats for forty pence, that were wont to be sold for four pence. Also the money was so sore clipped that there was no remedy but to have it renewed.'

Clipped? Yes, in the days of King John, when your silver crown was really worth its weight in silver, the coins were clipped for change. A little bit was clipped off, if you bought a groat's worth of goods; a bigger bit if you had spent a mark. Later in the year of the Great Frost, many an honest farmer who had to buy oats because the frost had killed his crops must have thrown up his hands at the price demanded by the merchant. 'What, forty pence the quarter, Simon?' cried he. 'I paid but the tenth part of that when good King Henry sat upon the throne.' 'True, Robin,' agreed the merchant, 'but since bad King John sits there now, there's a frost come over England.' And Farmer Robin groaned for the good old days long gone, while Merchant Simon added ten groats to his secret hoard, and gloated on good days to come.

JANUARY 15

The King Rides Forth

KING FROST rides forth in Europe
  With fist of shining mail:
'This is my hour' (he said) 'of power,
And men shall feel my flail.
I'll turn the rivers into rocks,
I'll seal the water-springs with blocks,
I'll drive the starving wolf-packs down
To prowl for prey about the town—
Yea, I will leave my toll of dead
Behind me where I ride' (he said)
'Even as Attila the Hun
Europe once did overrun,
And freeze with fear the lands where'er
He rode to slay and not to spare.
        Ho, winds, ho!
        Sound an icy blast!
        Bitter, bitter blow
        As the King rides past,
King Frost who numbs the mountain
And petrifies the vale,
And stuns the tribes of Europe
With his fist of mail!'

JANUARY 16
'Wolf-Month'

WE call it January. The Romans called this month after Janus, the god with two faces, one on each side of his head. The face at the back looked towards the year that was gone, the front face looked forward to the year to come.

But before the Romans brought his name among us, the Saxons called this the Wolf-Month, because the cold drove the wolves from the wastes, where they could not find animals to devour, to the hamlets where they lay in wait for men.

JANUARY 17
BENJAMIN FRANKLIN *born* 1706

The Water American

BENJAMIN FRANKLIN drank nothing but water all his life. He died an American citizen; but he was born an English subject, seventy years before he helped to draw up the Declaration of Independence; and long before that he travelled to London, and worked in a firm of English printers. It was from them that he got the name of 'The Water American'. The English printers drank beer before breakfast, beer before dinner, beer before supper, and beer with breakfast, dinner, and supper into the bargain. To them, a man who drank only water was a freak—'Yet,' said Benjamin Franklin, 'on one occasion I carried up and down stairs a large form of types in each hand, when others carried but one in both hands. They wondered to see that the *Water American* was stronger than themselves, who drank *strong* beer.'

JANUARY 18

The Death of Diving Mouse

ON the 18th of January 1835 Muk Coonee, the Red Indian Chief of the Michigan Tribe, sat at the bedside of his young Squaw, Diving Mouse. Diving Mouse was sick, and he knew she would not live. The bedroom was a poor lodging in London. Outside in the dirt of Waterloo Road, carts rattled over the cobbles, and street-sellers uttered their cries. In his palace over the river, King William the Fourth was waiting for the Chief, who had come from Michigan to sell him land; but what cared Muk Coonee while Diving Mouse lay dying?

The red woman raised her head, tired with the weight of its heavy black plaits. 'Muk Coonee! Little Boar!'

'Say, Diving Mouse.'

'Have you seen the White Chief?'

'Not yet. Let him wait.'

'He will be angry.'

'Let him be angry. More to Muk Coonee's heart than the White Chief is Diving Mouse. The White Medicine-Man has left this draught for her to drink.'

'No, Muk Coonee. If it is the Great Spirit's will that Diving Mouse shall return to him, he will not be pleased with her for averting her doom. It is strange that her doom should come on her among strangers. She would have liked to die in sight of the Great Lake, among the maize-fields. But the Great Spirit wills it otherwise. Little Boar!'

'Say, Diving Mouse.'

'Let there be ceremonies at my burial.'

[40]

'What ceremonies does Diving Mouse desire?'

'A silver plate on the box you lay me in. Let the box itself be ornamented. Dress me in my finest garments, paint my cheeks red, and lay a rich cloth on me. My ear-rings in my ears, leaves of laurel on my breast, and blossoms. For covering, the most splendid shawl you gave me. And throw a white rose after me, before the cold earth falls.'

King William in his palace, waiting on his throne with his crown on his head, what was he to Muk Coonee, the Michigan Brave?

All that Diving Mouse had desired was done. To-day her dust lies in St. John's Churchyard, in the Waterloo Road.

And Muk Coonee said: 'She who was all my earthly happiness is now under the earth. I never was a man of tears; but her loss made me shed many.'

JANUARY 19

Aquarius

(A Zodiac Song)

An old man with a water-jar
And beard as white as snow
In heaven moves from star to star
Spilling his overflow.

As along the channels chill
Out of the orifice
Aquarius' drops of water spill
They turn to stars of ice.

JANUARY 20

Pyrrhus and Cineas

EARLY in the year 281 B.C., King Pyrrhus of Epeirus determined to make war on Italy; he was a sort of cousin of Alexander the Great, and almost his equal in ambition and renown.

Nineteen hundred years later, the sixteenth-century poet, Thomas Traherne, was writing. Traherne was a man without a thought of ambition or fame; he knew that what you think and feel and see makes you happy, and not what you have. He had ten pounds when he died, and was perhaps one of the happiest men who ever lived. Among his writings is a talk between this same King Pyrrhus and a philosopher, which speaks for itself, and for Thomas Traherne too.

Pyrrhus the king sent for his friend Cineas the philosopher, and desired his counsel.

'On what matter?' asked Cineas.

'I intend to invade Italy.'

'To what purpose?'

'To conquer it.'

'And what will you do when you have conquered it?'

'Go to France, and conquer that.'

'And when you have conquered France?'

'Conquer Germany.'

'And what then?'

'Conquer Spain.'

'I perceive you mean to conquer all the world.'

'That is so.'

'What will you do when you have conquered all?'

[42]

'Return,' said the King, 'and enjoy myself in quiet in my own land.'

'So you may now,' said the Philosopher, 'without all this ado.'

JANUARY 21

ST. AGNES' DAY

Two Young Lambs

Two young lambs
  As white as may
Must leave their dams
  On Agnes' Day,
And go like little children home
To Saint Agnes' Church in Rome.
  There the Pope shall bless them,
  There shall men undress them.
  When the twain
  Go forth again
Leaving their spotlessness behind,
God send the shorn a tempering wind.

JANUARY 22
Birds of Sorrow
(A Chinese Proverb Tale)

IN the house of Wang the Mandarin a child was born. They called her Peach-Petal. Standing around the mother's bed, her friends praised the good fortune of the child born under so prosperous a roof. 'Her lot will be unalloyed happiness,' they said. But the mother, who had borne the child in bliss and pain, knew that no man's lot is unalloyed.

At night, as the mother lay neither asleep nor awake, she saw the Ladies of Sorrow and Joy enter the chamber with their birds in their hands. They came to the bedside and laid their fingers on the child, Joy saying, 'When you are sad, clap your hands!' and Sorrow, 'When you are glad, be still.' Then the Ladies let their birds fly, and went away.

Peach-Petal grew from infancy to childhood, and her days were made of light and shade. Around her head unseen flew the birds of sorrow and joy. Sometimes the wings of one fluttered her hair, and sometimes the other.

'Mother! how happy I am!' she cried in glee.

Then her mother, remembering, laid her hand on Peach-Petal's head. 'When you are happy, little daughter, be still, and the birds of joy will build their nests in your hair.'

But if Peach-Petal ran to her sobbing, 'Mother, I am unhappy!' her mother said, 'Clap your hands, little daughter, and sorrow will fly. You cannot stop the birds of sorrow from flying through your hair, but you need not let them nest there.'

[44]

JANUARY 23
Birds of Joy

THE Birds of Joy
Shall nest in my hair,
The Birds of Sorrow
Shall not rest there.
O Bird of Sorrow,
Take to wing!
Bird of Joy,
O sit and sing!

JANUARY 24
Skate and Sled

FROZEN are the gutters, frozen are the gardens,
Bitter is the touch of the iron garden-gates,
Ice upon the water thickens now and hardens
For every child in winter who owns a pair of skates.

Snow upon the hill-sides, drifts upon the meadows,
Heaven-sent to boys and girls for riding on the slopes;
Every child in winter who owns a plank or sled owes
Thanks again to Mother Goose for answering his hopes.

JANUARY 25

ST. PAUL'S DAY

Paul's Weather

A LONG time ago, when people believed in omens, fair or foul weather on St. Paul's Day was looked for as anxiously as fair or foul weather on St. Swithin's. But it wasn't only rain that mattered on St. Paul's; there was a different meaning in every sort of weather that fell on January the 25th.

The Merchant's Wife woke early, to run and put her head out of window. 'What's the day like, wife?' grunted the sleepy Merchant. 'Fair!' said she. 'That means a prosperous year, my duck!' said he. 'Then you can afford that new silk gown you promised me, my chuck!' said she.

Or perhaps the Farmer, rising earlier still, came groaning to his breakfast of beer and bacon. 'There's snow on the way, Moll, I see it travelling from the north. If snow falls on

Paul's Day, that means an unfruitful year.' 'Then do you be careful of the corn in the granary,' said prudent Moll, 'and I will be careful of the flour in the bin.'

Or the Soldier and his wife went together to the door, to see how the wind blew, and if it blew hard the Soldier's face brightened, and he cried: 'Wind on Paul's Day means war coming, sweetheart!' and in he went to polish his armour. But if the air was peaceful, she clasped her hands for thankfulness, and said nothing; but she thought: 'Praise God for no wind to-day and no war to-morrow.'

Or perhaps the birds of the air and the beasts of the field looked up in their turn, and if the sky was cloudy, or mist hung on the horizon, the birds shivered on the trees, and the cattle huddled closer together, for clouds meant great mortality among the creatures. But if the day was clear, birds twittered that sweet spring was on the way, and cows chewed placidly the cud of content.

JANUARY 26

Peep-Primrose

MY plot of earth as yet is bare
Of all the bulbs I planted there,
However busy round their roots,
My trees are innocent of shoots.

But by a sooty little stone
Where crouched a bunch of leaves alone,
This morning I stooped down to see,
And oh! Peep-Primrose looked at me.

JANUARY 27

Lewis Carroll Came Here To-day

(*Born* 1832)

'You are wise, Mr. Dodgson,' the young child said,
  'And your forehead is getting a wrinkle;
And yet you've so twinkling an eye in your head—
  I'm wondering what makes it twinkle?'

'In my youth,' Mr. Dodgson replied to the child,
  'I acquired mathematical habits
To keep my odd thoughts from becoming as wild
  As March Hares, and as frequent as Rabbits.'

'You are wise, Lewis Carroll,' the child said again,
  'And the College you live in is hoary;
But if you've such numbers of thoughts in your brain—
  Do you think you could tell me a story?'

'In my youth, if you must know the truth,' whispered he,
  'I kept those same thoughts very supple
By letting my stories run quite fancy-free—
  Allow me to tell you a couple!'

JANUARY 28

New Lights for Old

ON the cold dark night of 28 January 1807 a crowd of
people collected down the length of Pall Mall, from
St. James's Palace to Cockspur Street. Some of the people
were mocking, some were sceptical, some rather frightened;
but all of them were curious. For this German chap, Herr
Winser, had declared that the streets of London could be lit
with gas. He had been a long time in persuading the authorities to let him make his experiment, but at last he had succeeded; and to-night he was going to prove it.

'Impossible!' cried one of the watchers and waiters. 'Why,

even Humphrey Davy, who knows what gas *is*, says you can't light a street with it.'

'Absurd!' cried another. 'Sir Walter Scott wrote t'other day that Winser was a madman, who proposed to light all London up with smoke.'

'New-fangled,' muttered a lamp-lighter. 'The old oil lamps is good enough for me.'

'So dangerous!' twittered a lady. 'Why, even if it's *possible*, who'll ever dare to go near the gas-pipes, with fire running through 'em? We shall burn at a touch!'

And then—

'OH!' cried the crowd from St. James's to Cockspur Street. From end to end Pall Mall burst into a blaze of yellow lights, the first proud street that ever was lit by gas. In a few more years that chain of lights had caught in all the big towns of England and America—and nobody was burned when they touched the pipes.

JANUARY 29
Edward Lear Went Away To-day
(*Died* 1888)

THERE was an old fellow called Lear
Who wrote lots of rhymes like this here.
When they asked, 'Is it Cymric?'
He merely said, 'Lim'rick!'
That cryptic-elliptical Lear.

JANUARY 30

Everyday Word-Meanings: GAS

THREE hundred years ago a Dutch chemist called Van Helmont made experiments with coal and discovered that it would give off something if it was heated. This 'something' could not be seen, but it would burn when a light was put to it.

Now here was a new thing in the world; what was Van Helmont to do? He couldn't go on calling it just 'something', he must find a name for it. Every baby has a name given to it, and this 'something' was the chemist's baby, so to speak, just come into the world.

The nameless thing was invisible, like air; or like a man's spirit, which is inside a man's body. The chemist had learned how to release this airy spirit from the body of the coal. Then, perhaps, he said to himself:

'This something is the soul, or "ghost", of the coal! And it has come out of nowhere, as the world once came out of Chaos. What sort of name can I invent for it, so that people will understand what it is? Let me see, now: ghost-chaos! chaos-ghost! Ah, that's it! I will call this something *Gas*.'

So 'Gas' was born as a Dutch word. But it flew, like an airy spirit, across the sea from Holland to England, and settled in the body of our language.

JANUARY 31
Presents from Heaven

I WILL give you
Presents from heaven
If you go byeloo,
Mammy's wee lamb.
I will give you
Seventy-seven
Scales of the Fishes,
Curls of the Ram,
A drink from the Carrier's Water-jar,
The Hunter's Belt, and the Polar Star,
I will give you
Heaven, my heaven,
When you go byeloo,
Mammy's wee lamb.

FEBRUARY

FEBRUARY 1

Fair Maid of February

CROCUS for Saint Valentine,
Daisy for Saint Margaret,
April-blowing cardamine
  For the Virgin Mary;
But pearlier and earlier
Snowdrop comes at Candlemas,
The innocent our children call
  Fair Maid of February.

Thistles for Saint Barnaby,
Robert's herb and Christopher's,
For the good Saint Augustine
  The bell of Canterbury;
But lowlier and holier,
Snowdrop in your purity,
Ring your bell for Candlemas,
  Fair Maid of February.

FEBRUARY 2
Candlemas Day

IN the City of Rome
On Candlemas Day
The Pope blesses candles
And gives them away,
Till all, high and low,
Before him have passed,
The Cardinals first
And the Sacristan last.
Then the candles are lighted
So golden and gay,
To the sound of sweet singing
On Candlemas Day.

FEBRUARY 3
The Beau of Bath
BEAU NASH *died* 1761

BEAU NASH he was a gentleman
Who followed his own path.
He was the Pink of Fashion
And the Autocrat of Bath,
Where Belles and Macaronis
Who flocked to cut a dash
Could only cut their dash beneath
The thumb of Mr. Nash.

[54]

Beau Nash he ruled th' Assemblies
With his lightest nod or frown,
The Pump-Room was his Court-Room
In that noble Roman town,
Where Caesar and Augustus,
If they had come to splash,
Would not have splashed except beneath
The thumb of Mr. Nash.

FEBRUARY 4
Eve's Snowdrops

I HAVE heard a legend, but I don't know where it comes from, that the snow fell on Eve when she left Paradise. Out of the snow an Angel appeared to her, who took a handful of snowflakes, breathed on them, and let them fall at her feet, where they turned into flowers that did not grow even in Paradise. The Angel said, 'This is an earnest to thee and to Adam that the sun will follow the snow.' Then he vanished; and Eve, comforted, gathered her first snowdrops.

FEBRUARY 5
Morocco, the Dancing Horse

IT was on one February the fifth, in the reign of King Henry the Sixth, that a certain John French of Fleet Street gave his mother an inn with two names, to have and to hold to the end of her days. One of its names was *Savage's Inn*, the other *The Bell and the Hoop*. A hundred years later, to make matters short, the hostelry was known as the *Bell-Savage Inn*;

[55]

and here, in 1595, a horse called Morocco did various wonderful tricks to the customers who sat in the gallery all round the inn-yard. Morocco was a little chestnut nag, belonging to one Mr. Banks from Scotland.

'Now Morocco!' cried Mr. Banks, throwing down his glove, 'pick yon up—and carry it to my Lady Greensleeves.'

Morocco took the glove in his mouth, and carried it, sure enough, to a smiling girl in a green gown, who kissed him between the eyes; and when the nag had cantered back to his master with the glove—'Now Morocco!' he commanded, 'take it to the gallant with a rose in his cap.' Off went Morocco, and dropped it at the right gentleman's foot, who stuck his rose behind Morocco's ear to the applause of the crowd.

Meanwhile, Master Banks had filled the glove's mate with coins. 'Now Morocco! tell the brave company how many coins be here.' And the clever little nag rapped out the right number with his foot, while the world sat amazed.

'Now Morocco! run round the gallery and show us which of these gentlemen is the best lover of ladies.'

Round the yard galloped Morocco, and stopped to whinny at a fat merchant in a big ruff, which could not hide his blushes while the company tittered.

To end with, Morocco stood on his hind legs and danced the Canaries to the admiration of all. And one who came to clap his hands with the rest was Master Will Shakespeare, the playwright who used all he saw under the sun. So that when, in *Love's Labour's Lost*, a hard problem in arithmetic is propounded, Moth the saucy page declares: 'How easy it is the Dancing Horse will tell you.'

FEBRUARY 6

On Queen Anne

QUEEN ANNE *born* 1665

QUEEN Anne is—*Pho!*
   That's easy said!
Who doesn't know
Queen Anne is dead?
Nay, gossip, nay,
Abate your scorn!
Learn that to-day
Queen Anne is *born.*

FEBRUARY 7

The Odd Story of the Portland Vase

ON the 7th of February 1845 Mr. William Lloyd walked into the British Museum and smashed the Portland Vase into 2,000 little bits.

It was an odd affair altogether. The vase, very old, very valuable, very beautiful, and quite perfect, had been dug up in Rome three hundred years earlier—and of course it was very much older than that. It was so old that when it came to light, none of the know-alls could agree about it. They quarrelled about what it was made of, and what was the story told by the figures on it.

'It is made of amethyst!' cried one.

'Of agate!' said another.

'Of chalcedony!' swore a third.

'Of sardonyx!' declared a fourth.

'It tells the story of Theseus!' cried the first.

'Of Proserpine and Pluto!' said the second.

'Of the birth of a Roman Emperor!' swore the third—while the fourth sneered:

'Can't you see? It shows a lady consulting the great Doctor Galen, who is telling her that she is sick for love of a tight-rope walker!'

The disagreement of the experts was odd in itself. What was more odd was that Mr. William Lloyd, a mere member of the public, not only wanted to smash the precious vase, for no known reason whatever, but was actually able to do it. What was most odd was that, having smashed this costly antique into splinters, he was only sentenced to a fine.

True, he would have had to go to prison for a little while, if the fine wasn't paid. But the fine *was* paid—not by Mr. Lloyd, but, very oddly, by a gentleman who wouldn't give his name.

But *why* did Mr. Lloyd have that sudden impulse to smash the Portland Vase? Did he hate it at sight? Did he want to make people talk about him? Did he do it to prove what the vase was really made of? (It turned out to be dark blue glass, after all.) Nobody knows why he did it.

Perhaps quite the oddest thing of all was that the broken vase wasn't a Humpty-Dumpty, for a certain Mr. Doubleday came and put all the 2,000 pieces together again, so cleverly that it is almost impossible to see where it was broken.

> William Lloyd, in one of his fits,
> Smashed the Portland Vase to bits.
> William Lloyd was merely fined,
> The Vase was neatly re-combined,
> And nobody *yet* knows what annoyed
> The person known as William Lloyd.

FEBRUARY 8
Scotland's Mary
MARY QUEEN OF SCOTS *beheaded* 1587

SINCE Helen's beauty set great wars apace,
Had any Queen so fair and famed a face
As Scotland's Mary? Let a tear be shed!
To-day her fair face cannot save her head.

FEBRUARY 9
'Cabbage-Month'

WE call it February. But the Saxons called it Sprout-Kale, or Cabbage-Month, because the sprouting cabbage-stalk made a green time in the garden's lean time. The name may be a thousand years old, but the cabbages have outlived many kings; and when I walk in my kitchen-garden to-day, and see my sprouting kale (and not much else) waiting to go to the pot, I like to think that the Saxon goodwife blessed this stout vegetable as much as I do.

FEBRUARY 10
London's Lover
CHARLES LAMB *born* 1775

THEY say that the first seven years of a man's life plants the root for all the rest of it. Charles Lamb, who first saw light in Temple Lane near Crown Office Row, wrote of himself:

'I was born, and passed the first seven years of my life in the Temple. Its church, its halls, its gardens, its fountain, its river, I had almost said—for in those young years, what was this king of rivers to me but a stream that watered our pleasant places?—these are of my oldest recollections.'

Did Lamb know of that old saying when he made this picture of his first seven years? Whether he did or not, it is certain that he loved London all his life as few Londoners have before or since.

[60]

FEBRUARY 11
Peruquiers' Petition

'QUAH-QUAH!' said the Old Grey Goose to her Goslings, "'tis as true as sad and as sad as true that men live by many sorts of falseness, and none falser than hair, so that when His Majesty King George the Third took to wearing his own hair instead of a wig his gentlemen did likewise, and what was the wig-makers to do for a living, which on the Eleventh Day of February in Seventeen-Sixty-five, sent the London Peruke-makers as sure as I'm alive in a solemn deputation to the king of the nation with a piteous petition setting forth their condition, a-praying of His Majesty's Grace to wear a wig again when his subjects must needs follow suit, so saving the Peruquiers from ruin and starvation, which being made public set some wag publishing yet another petition from the London Body Carpenters, a-praying of His Majesty to wear a wooden leg, which to the best of my knowledge he never complied with, but the legs he was born with he lived and he died with, my Goslings,' said the Old Grey Goose, 'and so sure as my feathers aren't false my tale is true, quah-quah!'

(*And it really is.*)

FEBRUARY 12
Abe

ABRAHAM LINCOLN *born* 1809

ABE he war born in the Backwoods.
  Tough as hickory,
  Rough as thorn,
  In a log cabin
  Abe war born.

Abe he come to Election.
  Straight as the pine,
  Great as the gum.
  Into the White House
  Abe he come.

Abe he spoke for the Black Man.
  White as the birch,
  Right as the oak,
  For the slave's freedom
  Abe he spoke.

Abe he war felled in April.
  Said white birch,
        right oak,
        straight pine,
        great gum,
        tough hickory,
        rough thorn:
'Thar falls the best of us ever born.'

FEBRUARY 13

A Turkey-Stone for Mrs. Pepys

HAVE you chosen your Valentine for to-morrow? Shall you be chosen for a Valentine? Both, perhaps. For by the good old custom you can be a Valentine both ways; and if you were a boy in the days of Mr. Pepys, you had to pay for it. It wasn't a mere matter of buying a pretty card, or a comic one, and sending it, in feigned writing, to your boy or girl friend. On Valentine's Eve maids and bachelors gathered together, wrote their names on slips of paper, and dropped them into two boxes. The boys drew out the girls' names, one apiece, while the girls drew the boys' names; and so, by lot, you drew your own Valentine for yourself, and were drawn as Valentine to another willy-nilly. Then the fun began, and was kept up for several days; for in Valentine week each Valentine wore his partner's name pinned to his sleeve, and the bachelors had to make presents to the maids, and even give balls in their honour.

Let's take a peep at Mr. Samuel Pepys, writing in his famous Diary on Valentine's Day, 1667:

'This morning came up to my wife's bedside little Will Mercer to be her valentine, and brought her name written on blue paper in gold letters, done by himself, very pretty; and we were both well pleased with it. But I am also this year my wife's valentine, and it will cost me £5 but that I must have laid out if we had not been valentines.'

What Mr. Pepys gave to Mrs. Pepys was 'a Turkey-stone set with diamonds. It is fit the wretch should have something to content herself with'. But Samuel didn't get let off for his Five Pounds, after all; for 'Mrs. Pierce's little girl' had drawn *him* for her valentine, and there was another present to make. He probably gave her some pretty toy which cost less than a turquoise set with diamonds, and pleased her just as much.

FEBRUARY 14

SAINT VALENTINE'S DAY

Good Bishop Valentine

GOOD Bishop Valentine
Wandered all the night
Seeking out young lovers
And urging them to write:
With bags full of sugar-plums,
Rose and violet bowers,
Hearts, doves, true-love knots,
And lace-paper flowers.

Good Bishop Valentine
By the moon's beam
Went seeking out young maidens
And urging them to dream:
With ribbons for their ringlets,
Love's silken strings,
Orange-blossom posies
And gold wedding-rings.

Good Bishop Valentine

Phila Gough

E

FEBRUARY 15
Galileo Galilei
Born 1564

THE astronomer Galileo Galilei opened his eyes upon this planet in Pisa, where the Leaning Tower tilts like a telescope between heaven and earth. Galileo also turned his eyes to the planets in heaven, and from the stars learned secrets about our earth which men refused to believe. They would not believe that the world was round instead of flat. Ridiculous! as if one could stand steady on a ball! They could not believe that the earth rolled through space round the sun. Absurd! as if one would not be shaken off while it rolled! How much easier to believe that the sun rolled round the earth! Why, every day they saw with their own eyes how the sun rose over the edge of the earth, climbed to the top of the sky, and came down again. So there you were!

Galileo knew better. When he had made the first Italian telescope, and through it looked into heaven—'My eyes have seen another world', he wrote. And when he took his magic instrument to Venice, and led the Doge and Senators to gaze at the sun and moon from the top of the Campanile, their eyes were opened too, and Galileo Galilei was given money to pursue the path of starry knowledge.

Yet in the end he had to die for it; for when men are ignorant, great truths seem dangerous, and the man who offers them a new idea is the greatest danger of all. They forced Galileo to give the lie to his discovery. When he proclaimed, 'The earth moves!' they threatened him until he said, 'She does not move.' But out of hearing, to the day of his death, he whispered to himself: 'And still, she moves!'

FEBRUARY 16

Everyday Word-Meanings: CEILING

WHEN you stand like Galileo in the road and look up, your eyes go past the plane-trees on the pavement, the chimney-pots on the house-tops, they go even higher than the pigeon flying over the church spire, and come at last to rest on the sky.

When you stand in a room and look up, your eyes go past the clock on the mantelpiece and the picture on the wall, and come to rest on the ceiling.

You may even have had the fancy for yourself that the ceiling is the sky above the room, and that the sky is the ceiling over the earth. If so, it was no fancy, but the truth; for the word CEILING really does mean the sky, which we often call by another name: heaven.

Where did this word CEILING come from? out of which of the foreign fields that have given us so many of our words? It came from the old Latin field, the language of the Romans, who called heaven *Caelum*. When the Romans conquered France and entered the land, their words entered the language, and *Caelum* became *Ciel*, which in French means heaven.

Then France conquered England, and in turn brought its own words into the language; and *Ciel* became, in our tongue, not 'Heaven', which is the roof over the world, but 'Ceiling', which is the roof over each man's smaller world, the room he lives in. So now you see how, when you speak of the ceiling in English, you are speaking of the thing which in France means the sky.

In some old houses the ceiling was painted blue, like the

heavens, with fleecy clouds, or an angel or two flying across it; it may show silver stars, or the sun spreading his rays. We are not all lucky enough to have such a ceiling to our rooms; but if our homes are happy ones, it will not be hard to look up and see the ceiling as the heaven over our heads.

FEBRUARY 17
Saffron Walden

TO-DAY is Saint Flavian's Day, and the saffron crocus is Saint Flavian's flower, so now I'll write you a nursery rhyme for Saffron Walden in Essex.

Old man of Essex in the Wood,
  How came the Wood so green,
And how came this gold saffron-flood
  Of crocus in between?

'Why, first the Lord 'e made the wood
  So green without a flower,
An' then 'e made the crocus-bud
  All in a golden hour.

'Come Spring, the Lord walked in the Wood
  Filled full with crocus-shine,
'E saw that what 'e made wur good,
  An' said: This Wood is mine!
    An' ever after called 'un
    His Saffron Walden.'

FEBRUARY 18

The Treasure Island

ON the 18th of February 1935 the motor-drifter *Veracity*, Captain Arthur Macfarlane commanding, was being fitted out to go treasure-hunting off Cocos Island, the richest of islands in legends of undiscovered treasure.

Cocos was the Pirates' Paradise; many a buccaneer made it his head-quarters, while he went filibustering off the coast of Peru, where the Spaniards were in possession of the mines. The galleons commanded by the Spanish Dons sailed the seas with cargoes of gold ingots and 'pigs' of rough silver; besides which, the Dons had a fancy for travelling with chestfuls of jewels, and stores of costly wines, while their cabins gleamed with services of gold plate. So the Spanish galleons were the richest prizes that any pirate could hope to take on the high seas.

In about 1684 Captain Edward Davis, in the good ship *The Batchelor's Delight*, settled on Cocos Island, and sacked the city of Leon, on Lake Nicaragua. Result: five thousand pieces of eight for every man jack of his crew. As for his own share, he took so much that he had to leave most of it buried on the island; and Edward Davis's treasure is one of the legends of Cocos.

In the next century Captain Bartholomew Sharp, buccaneering off Panama, took the *San Pedro* (40,000 pieces of eight and a cargo of ingots), and the *Rosario*, with 700 pigs of silver from the mines, and money by the chestful. The crew mistook the rough silver for tin and, on returning to Cocos, dumped most of it into the sea. Another haul, waiting for somebody.

But the biggest treasure of all was buried there, about 1820, by Captain Thompson, of the merchant brig *Mary Dear*. He was, it seems, an honest man when the Spaniards living in Lima entrusted to him twelve million dollars' worth of gold and jewels. He buried it in Cocos; fell in with a pirate bearing the most piratical name of Benito Bonito; and turned pirate too. Benito came to grief, and Thompson with him; and he never succeeded in getting back to the fortune he had left on Cocos Island.

There it still lies, along of Captain Davis's and Captain Sharp's, for treasure-seekers to find. Or are they all legends?

FEBRUARY 19

'Do Yourself a Kindness, Sir'

(An Italian Proverb Tale)

A WELL-FED, well-clothed, well-off citizen was walking along a rough path in the hills of Tuscany. In his purse he had some twenty lire.

Towards him came an ill-fed, ill-clothed, ill-off man. His pale and bony face, sunken eyes, and stooping gait showed that if he had eaten at all in the past week, he had not eaten enough.

'This fellow', said the citizen to himself, 'is going to stop me. Not to rob—he is too feeble for that—but certainly to beg. Now what sort of kindness will he ask of me? Food? Work? Money? Money most likely; he'll pitch a fine tale of some sort, and I suppose I shall have to give him one of my lire.'

By this time the two men were face to face. The beggar raised his heavy eyes to the citizen's, and holding out his hand, said: 'Do yourself a kindness, sir.'

It seemed to the citizen that he was looking into his own eyes, and instead of one lira he gave the beggar ten.

FEBRUARY 20
The Kindness

THE kindness done
To any poor brother
Is done to yourself
More than another.

If a beggar stand
Like a hungry waiter,
Put in his hand.
Your need's the greater.

FEBRUARY 21
Alexander the Great and the Beggar

THE Great Alexander gives generously to a Beggar.
The Beggar says: 'It is too much.'
Alexander replies: 'It may be too much for you to receive, but it is not too much for me to give.'

FEBRUARY 22
'Away with it! quoth Washington'
GEORGE WASHINGTON born 1732

NO, George wasn't the Washington who said this, but it was for ever on the lips of one of his English forbears, a hundred years before he was born. Colonel Henry

[72]

Washington, who fought hotly for King Charles the First against the Roundheads, was so high-handed that he never stopped for any difficulty. When one arose, he promptly swept it aside; and 'Away with it! quoth Washington' became a slogan amongst his soldiers.

But in a few years, when Oliver Cromwell was saying 'Away with it!' to King Charles's head, a Cavalier Washington emigrated to America to found the family there. A hundred and twenty years later, it was his descendant, George, who was saying 'Away with it!' to George the Third of England; and down came the Union Jack, and up went the Stars and Stripes.

Now, the father of the Washington who emigrated in Cromwell's time was buried in Brington in Northampton-shire, and the shield of the Washingtons was on his tomb. Here is a picture of it.

Does anything strike you? And did it strike George Washington, when he said to himself: 'What shall our American flag be like?'

FEBRUARY 23

Pisces

(*A Zodiac Song*)

I SEE two fish swim in the sky
With twinkling tails
And sparkling scales.
One swims low and t'other swims high.
Those fishy twins
With glistening fins.
But which swims high,
And which swims low,
Never ask I,
For I don't know!

FEBRUARY 24

Who was George Frederick Handel?

HE was a musical composer, and a German. But he lived so long in England that he was almost English.

He was born in Saxony, on the 24th of February, 1685.

He composed sonatas at the age of 10.

He liked composing better than his dinner.

And in spite of this he became exceedingly fat.

At the age of 19 he fought a duel with another composer, with a sword in his hand, and a musical score under his coat.

The other composer ran him through—or would have, but his sword-point broke on the score.

He came to London in 1710, against the wishes of George, the Elector of Hanover.

He promised that he would go back to Germany soon.

But he liked England so much that he didn't go back.

He wrote such a wonderful *Te Deum* for the Peace of Utrecht that Queen Anne gave him a pension of £200 a year.

Then she died, and George, the Elector of Hanover, became George the First of England.

Handel remembered his broken promise, and scratched his wig.

But he composed his lovely *Water Music* for wind instruments, and had it played on the Thames during a Royal Progress of the King.

King George forgave him on the spot and doubled his pension.

He wrote his greatest work, the *Messiah*, in 1741.

London sneered at it.

So he went to Dublin, and played it in aid of the city prison.

When he came back to England, London flocked to hear it, and he flourished to the end of his life.

He endowed the Foundling Hospital with £7,000 and an organ, and had the *Messiah* played once a year in the Chapel.

He liked coffee and tobacco and the company of actors.

He played the harpsichord exquisitely and the organ grandly, but his hands were so fat that Quin the actor said his fingers were toes.

When his concerts went well his wig trembled with pleasure; when they went ill, the performers trembled with fear.

After a bad solo, he roared 'CHORUS!' in a voice of thunder.

He never married;

became blind;

died on Good Friday, 1759;

and is buried in Westminster Abbey.

FEBRUARY 25

Run to Church with a Frying-Pan

O N Pancake Tuesday in Olney, a little before noon, they
ring the Pancake Bell. Then Olney housewives hastily
mix their batter and toss their pancakes; for when the church
clock strikes twelve, these Buckinghamshire wives and maids
must

Run to Church with a Frying-Pan!
A Kiss for the Woman, a Cake for the Man.

Run to Church with a frying-pan,
    Never you lose a minute!
Run to Church with a frying-pan
    And a yellow pancake in it.
First to carry her pancake there,
    Though heavy or light she beat it,
Must toss her cake to the Bellringer,
    And the Bellringer must eat it.
Then be she madam or be she miss
    All breathless after rushing,
The Bellringer shall give her his kiss
    And never mind her blushing.

A Kiss for the Woman, a Cake for the Man--
Run to Church with a Frying-Pan!

[77]

FEBRUARY 26

Bread and Water

THE board is bare,
The revel is done,
Meagre the fare
For all and one.
Sackcloth for wear,
Ash on the hair,
The feast is ended,
The fast begun.
Crumb for my daughter,
Crust for my son,
Bread and water
For everyone.

FEBRUARY 27
Seventh Son

TRADITION says that there are four lucky days in February: the 10th, the 19th, the 27th, and the 28th. This is the third of February's Lucky Days, and as it has the luckiest of all numbers in it, I will make a song for the luckiest of all children, the seventh son of a seventh son.

Seventh Son of Seventh Son
Will be fortune's favoured one.
Pain and sickness will not linger
Where he lays his healing finger,
Pennies fallen in the street
Will roll underneath his feet.
And at fairy-time 'tis he
Will the lights of elfdom see.

Seventh Son of Seventh Son
Hath a strand of magic spun
In the woollen of his life.
He will wed a happy wife,
He will know the rainbow's worth
And the secret of the earth,
And a seeing eye will cast
On the future and the past.

Seventh Son of Seventh Son,
Thank your star if you are one.

FEBRUARY 28
Lucky Day

THIS is the Fourth Lucky Day in February.

And since every day is somebody's birthday, here is something for to-day's lucky child.

To the child who was born in Arles, in France, four things were brought: salt, bread, an egg, and a candle. And the saying ran:

> Sage comme le Sel,
> Bon comme le Pain,
> Plein comme un Oeuf,
> Droit comme un Bougie.

Which means:

> Wise as Salt,
> Good as Bread,
> Full as an Egg,
> Straight as a Candle.

Four things were also brought to the cradle of a new-born child in Westmorland in England: salt, bread, an egg, and a piece of silver. I know of no rhyme that accompanied these gifts; if there was one, 'pure as silver' may have been said instead of 'straight as a candle'.

And I have yet to discover what gifts, if any, were brought to the new-born child in Peru, Timbuktu, and Kalamazoo.

FEBRUARY 29

As Saint Patrick goes Walking

ONCE in four years you may wonder how Leap Year got its name, and the custom which allows all spinsters to leap at any bachelor, and claim a forfeit of him if he won't. Here's my favourite story about this, and if you don't believe it no bones will be broken.

As Saint Patrick goes walking on the banks of Lough Neagg, whom should he meet but Saint Bridget in tears.

'What is it, alanna?' says he.

'Oh sorrow,' says she, 'my nuns will be the death of me.'

'Why for?'

'They're wantin' the right to be married, and to ask the boys themselves.'

'Let them want,' says he, 'and stop weepin', alanna.'

'I can't,' says she.

'Then how would it be,' says he, 'if we let the colleens ask the boys once in seven years?'

'I daren't face them with anything so seldom,' says she. Then, taking Patrick's hand in hers, she starts to wheedle. 'Let you make it once in four years, darlint!' And Bridget gives his hand a good big squeeze.

'Squeeze me that way again,' says Patrick, 'and it not only shall be so, but I'll leap another day into the month to give them more of a chance.'

Bridget then asks, 'And if the boys say no?'

'The colleens may claim a forfeit.'

'And is this the month it is?'

'The very month.'

'And is this the extra day?'

'The day itself.'

'Then Patrick, me darlint, will ye marry me?'

'And what of my vow?' says he, taken aback.

'I can't help that,' says Bridget, 'and plaze for me forfeit I'll have a new silk gown.'

The story says that she got a kiss as well.

MARCH

MARCH 1

March, you old Blusterer

MARCH, you old blusterer,
  What will you bring?
Sunny days, stormy days,
  Under your wing?
No matter which it be,
  You will bring spring.

Whether Lion roaring comes
  Over bleak hills,
Whether Lamb bleating goes
  Seeking sweet rills,
You will bring primroses
  And daffodils.

[83]

Whether the earth shows a
White or green quilt,
Where in both hedge and tree
Men hear a lilt,
March, you old blusterer,
Nests will be built.

MARCH 2
'The Airgonauts'

'*INCROYABLE!*' cried the people of Paris, on the 2nd of March, 1784, as Blanchard, the aeronaut, went up in his balloon. Why, the crazy fellow had filled his balloon with gas! and furnished it with a pair of wings!! and a rudder!!! Did he suppose that men could really fly? This was a year of wonders in the air; ballooning was all the fashion; a novelty, of course, it couldn't last. But the world turned out to see these aeronauts, whom Horace Walpole labelled 'Airgonauts'.

'T'other night I diverted myself with a sort of meditation on future *airgonation*, supposing it will not only be perfected, but will depose navigation. . . . I supposed our seaports to become *deserted villages*; and Salisbury Plain, Newmarket Heath, and all downs (but *the* Downs), arising into dock-yards for aerial vessels. . . .

'To come to my ship-news: "The good balloon, Daedalus, Captain Wingate, will fly in a few days for China; he will stop at the Monument to take in passengers. Arrived on Brand-sands, the Vulture, Captain Nabob; the Tortoise snow from Lapland; the Dreadnought, from Mount Etna, Sir

SIC ITUR AD ASTRA

The Airgonauts

W. Hamilton commander; the Tympany, Montgolfier. Foundered in a hurricane, the Bird of Paradise, from Mount Ararat; the Bubble, Sheldon, took fire, and was burnt to her gallery; and the Phoenix is to be cut down to a second-rate." '

All the world laughed with Walpole at these 'Airgonauts', while they gaped at them; Monsieur Blanchard's wings and rudders did not work. Who ever supposed they would? Men fly? *Incroyable!*

MARCH 3
The Moon in Your Garden

ISN'T it time to think of planting crops?
'Yes,' said the old farmer from Carinthia, 'but take a hint and watch the moon in your garden. When she waxes, plant above the ground; when she wanes, plant below the ground. Put in potatoes with a waning moon; the roots take heart to go down as *she* goes down. But plant maize, peas, and beans when she is waxing, and they will follow her and come up full.'

That's what the farmers used to say in Austria, and so they still do, I believe.

MARCH 4

Everyday Word-Meanings: GARDEN

IF, while she was pegging out the washing in the yard, your mother had called over the wall to her neighbour: 'How big's your garden, Mrs. Brown?'—Mrs. Brown might call back: 'Oh, 'bout fifteen feet by eleven, I dare say.' But if mother had called instead: 'Mrs Brown, what's the girth of your garth?'—Mrs. Brown would probably have grinned, and called back: 'Who're you getting at?'

Yet round the words *Girth, Garth,* and *Garden* one meaning goes like a Girdle; and Girdle, Girth, Garth, and Garden are all to be found in your own Yard.

Yard is an early English word meaning an enclosed space. It is just the same word as Yard, the measure; for the Yard-stick, a rod of 36 inches, would be used to measure out the Yard-enclosure.

We seem to have got our word 'Yard' from the Norsemen, whose word for it is 'Gaard'. And Gaard brings us, on the one hand, into that pretty enclosed space we call a Garden, and on the other hand to the word 'Gird', which is only another word for surrounding or enclosing anything. The Girth of a thing is the size that is girded; and Garth was only another old form of Yard, or Garden. If mother, a thousand years ago, had called to her neighbour: 'What girth is your garth?' Mrs. Brown would have understood her at once.

Every house is the better for a garden, and luckily a 'garth' can be of any 'girth' you like; I mean, an enclosure can be of any size. If you have no garden, you can keep flowers in the yard. If you have no yard, you can grow them in a window-box. And if you have no window-box, then your 'garth' can be just the 'girth' of a flower-pot on the sill.

MARCH 5
He would make Music
DR. THOMAS ARNE *died* 1778

'MY son shall be a lawyer,' said Mr. Arne, the upholsterer.

'A musician, father!' pleaded Tom, who kept a spinet muffled in the garret and played it when the family was asleep.

'A lawyer or nothing!' vowed the upholsterer, and sent him to Eton, to be educated among gentlemen's sons; where Tom preferred playing the flute to learning Latin.

'Stop your tooting!' cried the young Etonians. 'Who wants to listen all day to a penny whistle? Stop it, Tom, or we'll tell on you!'

But Tom fluted on; the young gentlemen told; and the upholsterer fetched him away to be articled to a solicitor. For three years he stuck to his law-books by day, and by night he dressed up as a lackey, and sneaked into the gallery at the Opera, where liveried servants sat free. Or he slipped into the Crown and Anchor Tavern, where Michael Festing, who led the popular concerts, noticed him.

'Teach me the violin, sir!' begged Tom Arne; and Festing taught him, till the pupil out-played the master.

Old Arne the upholsterer dropped into the Tavern one

night, and when he saw his son, fiddle to chin, his eyes popped with rage; but at the end of the concert they were popping with pride.

'A musician or nothing, father!' vowed Tom Arne.

And so he was; and if he had not been, Britannia might never have ruled the waves in song; for Dr. Thomas Arne wrote her national anthem for *The Masque of Alfred,* in 1740. Then Garrick brought him and his fiddle to Drury Lane, where he made tunes for the Shakespearian productions: 'Where the bee sucks', 'Under the greenwood tree', 'Blow, blow, thou winter wind'. And, many years later, chose the blowiest month of the year to die in.

MARCH 6

'Cheep!'

THEY have found my ledge.
   'Cheep!' they say, *'cheep!'*
Round the edge
Of the curtain I peep,
Standing quite still
Whenever one comes
To the window-sill
For the new-strewn crumbs.
They fly so light,
They light so quick,
With all their might
Saying *'Cheep!'* as they pick,
'Cheep! cheep! cheep!'
In thanks and faith,
While I stand and peep
And hold my breath.

MARCH 7
'Length-Month'

THE Romans called it Martius, after the War-god, Mars, and for them it was the first month of the year, when the vigorous battle of life began again.

But the Saxons called it Lenet-Monat, or Length-Month, because now the days were lengthening after winter. This long-forgotten name for the month is not dead; it lives in the word Lent, which falls in March. So this first month of spring includes the spiritual Christian name in the martial pagan one, like a meeting of the Lamb with the Lion.

MARCH 8
Hero of Astley's

ON March the Eight as sure as fate
In Eighteen-thirty-four,
Two little chaps called Horncroft played
Upon the Pimlico shore.

The younger boy in boisterous joy
Fell in; his little pal
(Aged nine) jumped quick to pull him out
Of the Grosvenor Canal.

Alas! alas! it came to pass
They both sunk out of sight.
Help! help! the cry of passers-by
Rang out who saw their plight.

It seemed that they must drown that day,
When lo! at a lively jog
Mr. Ryan of Astley's Amphitheatre
Came up with his Newfoundland dog.

Where? where? cried he. *There! there!* cried they.
(One did a pebble throw.)
'In, Hero, in, and save the sons
Of Mr. Horncroft of Pimlico.'

The gallant hound with a single bound
Leapt into the water so cold.
He seized the breeches of the elder boy,
But the breeches did not hold.

He plunged anew, and this time drew
The elder Horncroft out.
'In, Hero, in!' Mr. Ryan cried again
With an encouraging shout.

Ere long the other lay with his brother
Upon the muddy banks,
And Mr. Horncroft of Pimlico
Could hardly express his thanks.

So that same night he did invite
Hero and Mr. Ryan
To sup with him at his residence
For saving his sons from dying.

Though a hundred years ago in Pimlico
He averted a tragedy ghastly,
Here's to Hero the noble Newfoundland
Of Mr. Ryan of Astley's.

MARCH 9
Who was William Cobbett?

An English cottager's son, born in Farnham, 9th March, 1763. Worked in the fields as a child, and learned reading and writing from his father in the evenings.

Became a gardener at Kew; then, at 17, enlisted in the infantry.

Went with the regiment to New Brunswick, where he became Sergeant-Major and kept the regimental accounts.

Went without food, to buy grammars, pens, and paper; and always got up at four o'clock in the morning.

One winter, saw the 13-year-old daughter of an artillery sergeant scrubbing her wash-tub in the snow, before daybreak; and said, 'That's the girl for me.'

When the Artillery went back to England, she went too; and for four years Cobbett posted her all his savings, to keep her from hard work.

On his return, found her a maid-of-all-work at £5 a year. She handed him the whole 150 guineas he had sent her; and they married.

Discovered dishonest officers in his regiment; procured his discharge, and then informed the War Office.

At the court-martial, false witnesses were produced against him and he was forced to fly to France.

Sailed for America in 1792, and began writing violent pamphlets on public affairs. Was prosecuted for libel, and fled back to England in 1800.

Started *The Weekly Register* and upheld radicalism; stood up fiercely for the poor, hit out hard, and suffered for his beliefs.

[93]

In 1810 was fined £1,000 for libel, and imprisoned for two years.

In 1817 avoided another imprisonment by returning to America.

In 1819 came back to England, bringing with him the bones of Thomas Paine.

Stood unsuccessfully for Parliament till 1832; then was returned for Oldham.

But, too old to stand the life, he died on June 18th, 1835.

He wrote many plain-spoken books on politics and the country, and sowed the seed of reforms that took place after his death.

MARCH 10
March Speaks

Ho-ah! ho!
  I crumble the crust!
A peck of my dust
Is worth a king's ransom!
  Ho-ah! ho!
Men sow in the dry,
And who but I
Makes the meadowland handsome?
I bark! I bluster! I bellow! I blow!
Harvests give thanks to me!
        Ho-ah! ho!

MARCH 11
The Beggar

A BEGGAR with a ragged jacket,
  And battered hat upon his head,
And matches in a little packet,
  Stood on the kerb, and nothing said.
He did not even raise his eye
As on my business I went by.

If he had asked, I might have hurried;
  If he had looked, I might have fled;
But just because he never worried,
  And stood quite still, and nothing said,
I found I could not pass him by,
I gave, and he took, silently.

MARCH 12
The Robin in the Airplane

BIRDS nest in all sorts of places. Crows in the elm-tops, swallows under the eaves, sky-larks flat on the grass, chaffinches in apple-trees, nightingales in oaks, sparrows in the hedge.

But some birds break away from the beaten track. Wrens have been known to nest in letter-boxes, and blackbirds in the bronze cocked hat of the Duke of Wellington's statue. A robin who fancied a farm-wagon found herself carted to Brighton and back again. And in the spring of 1939 a pair of pigeons made their nest and hatched their eggs in an arm-chair in Mr. and Mrs. Drinkwater's bungalow in Thundersley.

Oddest of all is the robin who that same year nested behind the engine of an aeroplane in Denham. Six times the nest was destroyed by the human airman, and six times the feathered airwoman rebuilt it. Then the man gave in, and let her lay her six eggs in her seventh nest. The hatching of the eggs was odder still: Mrs. Robin sat on her eggs till the plane went up, and while it soared in the sky the hot engine acted as foster-mother. When it came down to earth, the patient robin took up her duties again. The young robins were hatched between flights, and each as it saw the light could boast that it had already out-soared the golden eagle.

MARCH 13

Under my Lean-to

UNDER the roof of my lean-to,
  The spring in my heart exulting,
I have peeped out and seen two
  Plighted lovers consulting.
    'Shall we build *here*?
    Shall we build *here*?
    Shall we build *here*
    This year,
    My dear?
    Shall we see *here*
    Our comical wee
    Nestlings appear?
    Shall we, shall we,
    Shall we?'
Lovers, decide! decide it!
  Ah, if they only mean to
Build their sweet nest and hide it
  Under the roof of my lean-to!

MARCH 14

How the Princess got back her Appetite

WHEN Princess Marie Louise of Bulgaria turned five, she lost her appetite. She wouldn't eat this and she wouldn't eat that. She began to grow as thin as Augustus, who wouldn't eat his soup. What was to be done?

The Royal Doctor, the Royal Cook, and the Royal Nurse, thought and thought and thought. With the royal larder full, must the little Princess starve? At last King Boris her father hit on an idea.

He sent to the State Infant School for eight poor children whose mothers' larders were like Mother Hubbard's. He had the table spread with everything children like, and sat the poor ones round it, with the Princess among them. The poor ones fell to, and the Princess looked on. But she did not eat.

Next day the eight children came again, and gobbled as before. This time Marie Louise both looked and laughed. But still she didn't eat.

On the third day she was interested as well as tickled, and couldn't resist joining in the fun herself—just a little.

On the fifth day she made a proper meal.

On the sixth she ate heartily.

And on the last day of the week she had got her appetite back for keeps.

Which was very nice for her, and for the King and Queen, and the Royal Doctor, the Royal Cook, and the Royal Nurse.

And I hope it went on being nice for the eight poor children who had given back the little Princess her appetite.

MARCH 15
City of London Pie
SIR THEODORE MAYERNE *died* 1655

SIX years after Charles the First lost his head in Whitehall, his physician, Sir Theodore Mayerne, died of drinking bad wine in the Strand. That at least is what he declared had finished him when he lay dying in his house in Chelsea. 'Good wine,' said this good-liver of 82, 'is slow poison. I have drunk it all my life and it has not killed me yet. But bad wine is sudden death.'

The wonder is that he had not long ago died of good feeding. For he has left behind him the best cookery-book of his century, the *Archimagirus Anglo-Gallicus*, whose title alone might give a man indigestion; and the recipes are as elaborate as the title. The first and best of them he dedicated to the City of London, where this jolly old knight had often gorged with the Lord Mayor; and here is Sir Theodore Mayerne's recipe for

A CITY OF LONDON PIE

Take eight marrow bones, eighteen sparrows, one pound of potatoes, a quarter of a pound of eringoes, two ounces of lettuce stalks, forty chestnuts, half a pound of dates, a peck of oysters, a quarter of a pound of preserved citron, three artichokes, twelve eggs, two sliced lemons, a handful of pickled barberries, a quarter of an ounce of whole pepper, half an ounce of sliced nutmeg, half an ounce of whole cinnamon, a quarter of an ounce of whole cloves, half an ounce of mace, and a quarter of a pound of currants. Liquor when it is baked, with white wine, butter and sugar.'

And now, go and make it.

MARCH 16
March Hair

IT was no fun for a young lady to be out in a March gale in London in 1795, when women's wigs were so tall that they were a positive danger. *The Times* of that year reports:

'A young lady only ten feet high was overset in one of the late gales of wind in Portland Place, and the upper mast of her feather blown upon Hampstead Hill'—

some four or five miles away.

But it must have been fun on a Sunday to be a little girl in church, sitting behind one of these fine ladies, wearing a tower of wool, horsehair, and powder-paste, bedecked all over with ornaments in the shape of bird-cages, coaches, and ships. It cost so much to dress these silly contraptions that the sillier ladies wore them day and night, and sat upright in bed wearing nightcaps of silver wire to keep out the rats, and a mousetrap on their pillows; for wool and paste attracted mice like a larder. But in spite of all precautions, a mouse sometimes slipped inside the wig while the lady dozed, and made its nest there. And it is told of one little girl, in the eighteenth century, that she sat in her pew on Sunday, and watched with delight the little mouse popping in and out of the tower of hair in the next pew, and quite forgot to attend to the parson's sermon on Vanity.

MARCH 17

Long Monday

WHEN the blessed Saint Patrick chased the reptiles out of Eire, there was in the Galtee Mountains one monstrous serpent that looked like being too much for him entirely. So the Saint took a chain to him, and harnessed him under one of Galtee's seven lakes, the one called Lough Dilveen, saying, 'Stay there, ye spalpeen.' 'How long for, Pathrick?' asked the Serpent. 'Till Monday,' said the Saint.

Every Monday morning from that time the Serpent lifts his head out of the Lough, and calls in the Erse tongue, 'It's a long Monday, Pathrick.' But he gets no answer, and goes down again.

If you do not believe me, let you walk by Lough Dilveen any sunrise after Sunday, and you'll soon see if I've told the truth or not.

MARCH 18
Aries
(*A Zodiac Song*)

RAMPANT Ram!
Rumbustious Ram!
Rugged and rampageous Ram!
Romping, ramping,
Rumpling, rambling,
Roistering, rollicking,
Rude, rapacious,
Rough-and-tumble ragamuffin,
Rampant and rumbustious Ram!

MARCH 19
Narcissus Fields

THE fields are in flower in the West,
The great narcissus fields.
The green grass-wave has a foaming crest,
And the breath of Cornwall yields
A tide of scent that flows
Over the seaweed smell;
'Twixt island and mainland it blows,
Sea-salt and asphodel:

As when, so long ago,
Olaf the Viking rover
Sailed to an isle he did not know,
And the flower breathed like a lover,
Wooing the pagan king
To light on Columba's shore.
The pagan came from the Cornish spring
Christian for evermore.

For the gentleness of the flower
Overwhelms the ocean-crest,
And Christ still walks on the wave this hour
When the fields breathe in the West.

MARCH 20

Samuel Jones, his Goose, and his Bees

'QUAH-QUAH!' said the Old Grey Goose to her Goslings,
'truth is truth and lies is lies, and as true as I'm no gander,
when Mr. Samuel Jones of Bath, that lover of geese and bees,
sat in his chair with Susie his goose in his lap, and tinkled
a bell, out swarmed his bees from their hives to cluster all
over him as though he was their queen, till one March
Sam died at the ripe old age of three-and-eighty years, and
two days after, Susie, having no heart to live without him,
died too, and a day after *that*, when they came to lay flowers
on his grave, it was humming from head to foot with a
swarm of bees, and if that's no sign, my goslings,' said the
Old Grey Goose, 'that Sam Jones isn't eating honey in heaven
with Susie on his knee, may I be choked with my longest
tail-feather, quah-quah!'

(*And may I be too, for the tale is as true as print.*)

MARCH 21
A Morning Song
(*For the First Day of Spring*)

Morning has broken
  Like the first morning,
Blackbird has spoken
  Like the first bird.
Praise for the singing!
Praise for the morning!
Praise for them, springing
  From the First Word.

Sweet the rain's new fall
Sunlit from heaven,
Like the first dewfall
  In the first hour.
Praise for the sweetness
Of the wet garden,
Sprung in completeness
  From the first shower.

Mine is the sunlight!
Mine is the morning
Born of the one light
  Eden saw play.
Praise with elation,
Praise every morning
Spring's re-creation
  Of the First Day!

MARCH 22
Randolph Caldecott
(*Born* 1846)

CALDECOTT'S pencil was fine and free,
Caldecott's brush was coloured and clear,
Caldecott drew for you and me
Childhood's country from earth to sky.
Whatever was sung for childhood's ear
Caldecott painted for childhood's eye.

MARCH 23
MOTHERING SUNDAY

The Birth of the Simnel Cake

'BOIL it!' said Simon.
'Bake it!' said Nelly.
'You're wrong!' said he.
'I'm right!' said she.
'Take that!' said he.
'And that!' said she.
And so the quarrel began.

What was the quarrel about? A cake, my dears, no more
and no less than a cake. And yet it started in a fit of loving-
kindness. For Simon and Nelly, that ancient Shropshire
goodman and his wife, were looking for their children to
come gathering home as usual one Sunday when Lent was
running out; and Nelly, a frugal soul, fetched the last of the
unleavened dough to make a family cake.

[106]

'Plain fare,' said Simon.
'Too plain,' said Nelly.
'Plum-pudden?' said he.
'From Yule,' said she.
''Twould help,' said he.
'A lot,' said she.

And Nelly fetched the left-over Christmas pudding, and made a ball of the dough with the pudding inside. What a surprise for her boys and girls on Mothering Sunday! But how to cook this new sort of pudding-cake? Simon swore that a pudding should always be boiled; and Nelly vowed that a cake could only be baked; and very soon they were at it hammer and tongs. Nelly threw the wooden stool at Simon's wooden head, and Simon laid the stout besom across Nelly's buxom shoulders; and between them they managed to smash a bowl of eggs.

'Enough!' said Nelly.
'And more!' said Simon.
'Boil first,' said she.
'Bake second,' said he.
'You're right,' said she.
'And you,' said he.
And so the quarrel was mended.

Simon fed the fire with the stool and the besom, while Nelly glazed the cake with the broken yolks and whites; then the pudding-cake was boiled in the pot and baked in the oven, and so the first Mothering-Sunday-Cake was born.

So good it was that their children spread its fame, and christened it Sim-Nel on the spot; for (said they) such a cake should only be named after both its makers, who had conceived it in such perfect agreement.

'That's so!' said Sim.
'And *so*!' said Nell.

And as Simnel the cake is known to this very day.

MARCH 24
Twelve Daisies

How many daisies can you count on your lawn?
When you can count twelve daisies, Spring has come.

MARCH 25
Lady Day

Here's Lady Day.
Go meekly,
Think sweetly,
Talk kindly,
Look mildly,
And love your baby
Like Our Lady
On Lady Day.

MARCH 26
The Quarryman and the Trees

A FRIEND who had lived for some time on a Derbyshire hill-side told me that he had there made friends with a quarryman whose talk was worth listening to. But he had a weakness, he couldn't keep off the drink, and had blown out one of his eyes with dynamite through being tipsy at work.

'I often told him what a fool he was to spend his time and money in the way he did; all he would say was, "I know it— but there it is." Then early in the year I began to notice that his eye and complexion cleared; and I saw to my surprise that he was sober. "What's come over you," I asked, "that you keep off the drink now?" "Ay," said he, "I can, at this time o' year." "What has the time of year to do with it?" I asked. "Well, it's like this," he told me. "In two months' time 'twill be spring, and I'm a-saving up my money to take a week off my work, so as I'll be able to go into the woods and *listen to the trees grow*."'

MARCH 27
'Every Man loves the Tree that gives him Shelter'
(A Russian Proverb Tale)

G REAT-GRANDFATHER planted an acorn the day Grandfather was born, and Grandfather was forty years old when Father was born, and ninety years and two days when Vanya saw the light. The first thing Vanya remembered of his Grandfather was seeing him sitting on a hot day in the shade of the fine broad oak at the end of the garden, sucking his old clay pipe, and crumbling a bit of bread for the birds, who no more feared the old boy than if he had been a branch of the tree itself. Often the pipe was empty, but still he sucked away; and after the bread was scattered his withered fingers went on crumbling at nothing, while he sat nodding and smiling placidly at the sun on the grass beyond his thick green shelter. First Vanya would be left beside him in an old sugar-box on wheels, which Grandfather pushed a little to and fro. Later, the child sat playing in the shade with the old man, the one as contented as the other.

One day Vanya looked from the oak-shade to his mother pegging out the washing in the sun, and he said, 'I like my mother best of things in the world.'

'That's right,' said Grandfather. 'Your mother's yer shelter, Vanya.'

'What do you like best, grandad?'

'My tree,' said Grandfather.

Father, passing with a barrow-load of weeds, called out, 'That's right, daddy! every man loves the tree that gives him shelter.'

Then Grandfather felt in his pocket and pulled out an acorn. 'Plant that,' he said to Vanya, 'and when your mother's no more and you're an old dad like me, you'll not want for shelter till the earth is your roof.'

MARCH 28
An Old Man's Epitaph

WHEN I was young I planted thee,
   And thou wast younger yet than me.
From every harm I sheltered thee
That might have nipped thy life, my tree.
I fostered thee and cared for thee
When thou wast weaker yet than me.
I passed my prime of life by thee
Ere thou hadst reached thy prime, my tree.
My time then came to fail by thee
Who wast become more strong than me,
And in my death I turned to thee
Whose years will outlive mine, my tree.
Under the earth I dug for thee
I lay me down—oh shelter me!
That life with which I nurtured thee
Take to thyself at last, my tree.

MARCH 29

EMMANUEL SWEDENBORG *died* 1772

Angels' Spring-time

IN the eighteenth century there lived in Sweden a great man called Emmanuel Swedenborg. For the greater part of his life he was a man of science, an expert in metals and minerals, but when he had passed the age of fifty a great change took place in his mind. He tells us that he often saw and spoke with angels, and made visits in his spirit to Heaven.

On one of these journeys he found himself in a large meadow, where a crowd of angels were looking on at some games. He joined the crowd and watched with them. What struck him most was that these sports were being ordered by very young angels, who seemed, indeed, like little children. So he turned to an elderly angel in the crowd, and asked him why those young children should control the game.

'O Sir!' answered the angel, 'those that you take to be children are really the oldest and the wisest amongst us. You must know that to grow old in heaven is to grow young; for the Angels of God are always advancing to the spring-time of their youth.'

MARCH 30

Fernando's Gratitude

AFTER Master Francis Pretty, of Eye in Suffolk, came back in 1588 from his prosperous voyage in the South Sea under Thomas Candish Esquire of Trimley, many an eager young Elizabethan must have pestered him for tales of his adventures, and heard him speak in this wise.

'On the thirtieth day of March, a year gone by, our three ships came into the Bay of Quintero. We had with us the Spaniard Fernando, that we had found starving among four hundred others at the mouth of the straits, who in his gratitude swore to us and to our general that he would die for us before he would prove false. That day as we came to anchor we espied a neatherd sleeping on the point of the hill; who, waking before we could come to shore, sprang on a grazing horse, and rode off like the wind. We were short of victuals and water, and this was a land of fresh rivers, well-stored with coneys, hares, and partridges; so our general took some thirty of us ashore, Fernando among us. We had not been an hour on land when there came three Spanish horsemen riding hard upon us with bright swords; but seeing our numbers they kept their distance and made signs. Our general sent Fernando, with two English shot, to parley with them, and make known our needs, and Fernando returned saying they would provide us with all the victual we required. Our general then dispatched Fernando with another message, but this time the Spaniards signalled that he must come alone; so our shot stayed apart while Fernando went forward. From our distance we saw them speak for but a moment with our fellow; when suddenly Fernando leaped behind upon one of their horses, and away they sped, four Spaniards instead of three. So much for his deep and damnable oaths of gratitude!'

MARCH 31
March, blow by!

MARCH, blow by
With your stormy grey eye!
April, run in
With your pear-blossom skin!
  The catkin is shaking
  A powder of gold,
  The daisy is breaking
  A way through the mould,
  The chaffinch is taking
  Her morsel of moss,
  The wind is making
  The rookery toss.
March, goodbye
To your stormy grey eye!
April, begin
With the bloom on your chin!

APRIL

APRIL 1
April Fool!

WHO will be an April Fool?
Do not fear the jest that tricks,
He who keeps his reason cool
In the rut of winter sticks.
  Each one t'other's wit out-matching
  In the game of April-catching,
Set for friends your nonsense-snares,
Catch them, and be caught by theirs.
Ere the clock has come to noon,
Be a loon and make a loon.
Do you live by solemn rule?
        Cuckoo!
        Cuckoo!
            April Fool!

APRIL 2

The Shoemaker's Child

IN Odense on the green island of Funen, at the beginning of the nineteenth century, lived a young shoemaker and his wife, whose name was Andersen. The man had a mind full of poetry, the woman a heart full of love. On the 2nd of April 1805 a son was born to them who cried even more than most babies. So loud he cried at his own christening that the pastor said crossly, 'The infant yowls like a cat!'

The mother dropped her eyes, ashamed; but the godfather, a poor emigrant called Gomar, patted her arm and whispered, 'The louder he cries while young, the sweeter he'll sing when old'.

They gave the child the names of Hans Christian.

The room Hans first knew was filled with the shoemaker's

[116]

bench, the big bed, and his own cradle; pictures hung on the walls, a cupboard of song-books over the bench, gay plates and bright pans filled the shelves, and between the gutters on the roof was a chest full of earth, in which his mother grew her garden.

As well as a wise father and a simple mother, Hans had a grandmother who tended the garden of an asylum. Twice a year, when she made bonfires of green weeds and pea-straw, she took Hans with her to feed the fire, eat nice food, play with chalk, and rest on the heaps of leaves.

The spinning-wheels hummed in the old women's rooms near by; the child awoke, crept to the door, and peeped in. The old ones welcomed him, and soon he was chalking pictures on the door for the spinners, who paid him back with remembered tales and legends—'and thus', says Hans Christian Andersen, 'a world as rich as that of the Thousand and One Nights was revealed to me'.

APRIL 3
The Looby Loons

SAID This Looby Loon to That Looby Loon:
'I'll ask you a Riddle.'
Said That Looby Loon to This Looby Loon:
  'What shall I get if I don't guess your Riddle?'
Said This Looby Loon to That Looby Loon:
  'What I've got in my pocket.'
Said That Looby Loon to This Looby Loon:
  'Ask me your Riddle.'

Then This Looby Loon asked That Looby Loon this Riddle:
   'Queen Mary she had it before, poor thing!
   King William he had it behind, poor thing!
   Queen Anne never had it at all, poor thing!
   Now see if you're able to find the thing!'
Then That Looby Loon said: 'It's a pickle in a tea-caddy.'
   'No it's not!'
'It's an elephant's breath.'
   'No it's not!'
'It must be Adam's Grandmother.'
   'No it's not!'
'Well, what is it, then?'
   'It's the Letter M.'
'Why?'
   'Never ask me,' said This One.
'I won't then,' said That One.
   Then This Looby Loon gave That Looby Loon what he
had in his pocket, and what This Looby Loon had in his
pocket was a hole. That Looby Loon was so pleased that he
put the hole in his own pocket, and lost all his pocket-money
on the way home.

APRIL 4
The King's Fool

WHEN James the First of England was Jamie the Sixth of Scotland, young Archie Armstrong sat rocking a cradle in the dark corner of his hut on the moors. A simple fool was Archie, as you could tell by his silly song.

Over the moors rode the King's officers of justice, and into the hut they burst; but seeing only a foolish boy —'In the name of King James,' cried they, 'where's the shepherd?'

'The guidmon's awa',' said Archie vacantly, and went on crooning his lullaby.

'A body was seen coming this way with a sheep on his shoulders, laddie.'

'Oo-ay?' said Archie.

'The penalty for sheep-stealing is death.'

'Oo-ay?' said Archie.

The officers gave the loon up as a bad job, and searched the cottage, in vain. As they were about to go, one of them stepped to the cradle asking, 'Is the bairn a girl or a boy?'

'A dinna ken,' mumbled Archie.

'No wonder!' said the officer, "tis a fine fat ewe.' The stolen sheep was dragged out of the cradle, and Archie himself was dragged before King James, sitting in justice at Jedburgh. When the young fool had been found guilty and condemned to death—

'Ha'e ye onything tae say, Archie Armstrong?' asked King James.

'Oo-ay!' said Archie. 'Tak peety on a puir ignoramus, Sir

King, that has haird tell o' the Bible and never read it. For my soul's weal, let me read the Book before I dee.'

'So good a request must be granted,' said James.

'On the King's honour?' said Archie.

'On the King's honour,' said James.

'Then Diel tak me,' said Archie, 'gin I ever read a word o't as lang as my een are open!'

King Jamie of Scotland (and James of England) threw back his head and laughed. 'Archie,' said he, 'ye've come to court in Scotland; now ye shall come to Court in London, and be my jester till your een be shut.'

And that's how King James got his fool.

APRIL 5

A Quill for John Stow

ON the Fifth Day of April
The Lord Mayor shall go
To place a new quill
In the hand of John Stow.
John's hand is of stone
That once was alive,
And never used quill
After Sixteen-O-Five.
But it wrote down the story,
With inkpot and quill,
Of London for ever
Before it grew still:
And the Fifth Day of April
For ever since then
The Lord Mayor of London
Gives John a new pen.

APRIL 6

A Ballad of Palm Sunday

'TWAS of a cold Palm Sunday,
   Palm Sunday in the morn,
The White Rose of York
Proved the Red Rose's thorn;
The Red Rose of Lancaster
Did bleed upon the snow,
When the Sixth of the Henrys
Was harried to his woe.

'Twas on the Field of Towton,
Of Towton in the north,
The White Rose of York
Against the Red came forth;
By the town of Tadcaster
They fought the hardest fray
Since William of Normandy
Laid Harold on the clay.

Oh Margaret the Queen
Across the border's flown!
Oh the Kingmaker has set
A new King on the throne!
Oh gentle Henry Windsor
Is languishing in thrall!
Oh the White Rose shall flourish
And the Red Rose fall.

APRIL 7
A Wife for Sale

ON 7 April 1832 Mary Anne Thomson stood for sale in Carlisle market: a straw halter round her neck, her best frock on her back, and as cross as two sticks. Her husband, Joseph Thomson, who after three years had had enough of her, set her in an oaken chair, and cried to the crowd:

'Gentlemen! I have to offer to your notice my wife, Mary Anne Thomson, whom I mean to sell to the highest and fairest bidder. Gentlemen! she has been to me only a born serpent. I took her for my comfort, and the good of my home; but she became my tormentor, a domestic curse, a night invasion, and a daily devil. Gentlemen! may God deliver us from troublesome wives and frolicsome women! Avoid them as you would a mad dog, a roaring lion, a loaded pistol, cholera morbus, Mount Etna, or any other pestilential thing in nature. Now I have shown you the dark side of my wife, and told you her faults and failings, I will introduce the bright and sunny side of her, and explain her qualifications and goodness. She can read novels and milk cows; she can laugh and weep with the same ease that you could take a glass of ale when thirsty. She can make butter and scold the maid; she can sing Moore's melodies, and plait her frills and caps; she cannot make rum, gin, or whisky, but she is a good judge of the quality from long experience in tasting them. I therefore offer her with all her perfections and imperfections, for the sum of fifty shillings.'

For an hour Farmer Thomson stood and haggled with the reluctant bidders. At last one Henry Mears cried, 'Twenty shillings!' 'And your dog!' cried Joseph Thomson. 'A bargain!' said Mears. He handed over his Newfoundland dog; Thomson handed over Mary Anne; and so they went their ways.

APRIL 8
Cock and Hen
(*A Russian Proverb Tale*)

THE Cock and his Hen were waiting for their great moment. One stood on top of the dungheap contemplating the sky, the other squatted at the foot considering the earth. Suddenly the Cock let out a crow, as a blaze of light swelled over the clouds. At the same instant the Hen let out a cackle, as a blaze of delight filled her feathers.

'The great yolk!' crowed the Cock.

'The little yolk!' clucked the Hen.

'What a fuss you make about that little yolk of yours,' observed the Cock stepping down, 'as though it wasn't anybody's everyday job.'

'And how high-and-mighty we are about the big yolk up there,' retorted the Hen, 'to-doing over what everybody can see for himself with his own eyes.'

'Crowing's an art,' said the Cock, 'and I'd like to hear you try it!'

'And laying's a gift,' said the Hen, 'and I'd be sorry to see you attempt it!'

The argument rankled so that next morning found the Hen

on top of the dungheap and the Cock at the foot. But when the sun came up the Hen's failure to crow became the joke of the farm-yard, and when it went down again the Cock's failure to lay was its gossip.

'Get up do!' scolded the Hen. 'You're a scandal to my nest.'

'Come off it, you!' scoffed the Cock. 'You're shaming my dungheap.'

And old Neddy the donkey, with his chin on the gate, looked from under his tousel of hair with his sleepy patient eyes, and said: 'Stick to your jobs, my dears, and do what's in you to do. If you're a cock, crow. If you're a hen, lay eggs.'

APRIL 9
What They Do

COCKS crow,
Hens lay.
Cocks know
Break-o'-day,
Hens tell
Break-o'-shell.
Cocks crow,
Hens lay.

APRIL 10
Hannibal Jones

HANNIBAL JONES was fond of eggs.
His breakfast every day was eggs.
He kept no chickens who laid his eggs,
He bought no eggs, he borrowed no eggs,
He stole no eggs and was given no eggs.
How did Hannibal Jones get eggs?

(Go on a bit and you'll see.)

APRIL 11

Molly Grime

SEVEN Old Maids
Once on a time
Came of Good Friday
To wash Molly Grime.
The water for washing
Was fetched from Newéll,
And who Molly Grime was
I never heard tell.

Seven Old Maids
Got when they came
Seven new shillings
In charity's name.
God bless the water,
God bless the rhyme,
And God bless the Old Maids
That washed Molly Grime.

Nursery rhymes often set us guessing where they came from. We seldom know who wrote them, though we sometimes know whom they were about. Jack Horner was a real person, and so was the King of Spain's Daughter in 'I had a little Nut-tree', and the Fine Lady who rode-a-cock-horse to Banbury Cross. Something that had happened, or perhaps just a name, used to set the old nursery rhymesters doing their little dance and humming their little tune, for a couple of moments—then off they hop, leaving us wondering.

Now if you are wondering about the Seven Old Maids in the nursery rhyme for Good Friday, I can tell you something about them. They lived in the village of Glentham in Lincolnshire, hundreds of years ago, and in Glentham Church there was a figure known as Molly Grime. And some charitable person left in his will seven shillings a year, one apiece for seven old maids of Glentham, who should come on Good Friday to wash Molly Grime with water from Newell Well. This custom has now died out, and that is as much as I know.

There's a lot I don't know. I don't know who Molly Grime was. I don't know if she was made of wood or stone. I don't know why she had to be washed. But I do know why you have never heard this particular nursery rhyme before. It is because I wrote it myself, when I chanced on this old custom in a book. Molly Grime—the Seven Old Maids—the Seven New Shillings—the Water from Newell Well—and Good Friday morning: all set me doing my little dance and tune. And so, off I hop!

APRIL 12

The Flowering Hills

OH, flowering hills! oh flowering hills!
See, the wild plums in blossom stand,
And the wind-shaken cherry spills
Her flaky petals on the land.

The swelling countryside has been
Moulded beneath a cloudy mound
Of bloom that hides the dawn of green
And coloured blossoms on the ground.

It will not stay. It cannot stay.
But for a moment from the plain
Rising the sweet year has its way,
And all the hills have flowered again.

APRIL 13

Upon an Easter Morning

UPON an Easter Morning,
  So early in the day,
The bird raised up his whistle
To tune the night away,
The field raised up its grassblade
Of emerald anew,
The garden raised its flower,
The river raised its dew.

Upon an Easter Morning,
So early in the day,
The organ in the chancel
Sang both grand and gay,
The people on the causey,
The cattle in the pen,
Heard the pipes of heaven
Rising up again.

The light went like a ladder
From valley-bed to sky,
The lark went like a seraph
Beyond the mortal eye.
The wind went like a spirit
To blow the dust away,
Upon an Easter Morning
So early in the day.

APRIL 14

First Catch Your Hare

*W*HEN *does the rent fall due of the Parson's glebe*
                    At Coleshill in Warwickshire?
On Easter Monday Morning,
Before the clock in the tower strikes ten
                    At Coleshill in Warwickshire.

What is the rent of the Parson's glebe
                    At Coleshill in Warwickshire?
A calf's head,
A hundred eggs,
And four pence,
Paid down before the clock in the tower strikes ten,
On Easter Monday Morning,
                    At Coleshill in Warwickshire.

Who gets the rent of the Parson's glebe
                    At Coleshill in Warwickshire?
The very first man who catches a hare
And brings it to the Parson's door
For a calf's head,
A hundred eggs,
And four pence,
Before the clock in the tower strikes ten
On Easter Monday Morning,
                    At Coleshill in Warwickshire.

APRIL 15

ABRAHAM LINCOLN *was assassinated* 1865

'Don't badger them'

WHEN Abraham Lincoln was elected President at the outbreak of the Civil War, Blondin the tightrope-walker was at the zenith of his fame. He had performed his most tremendous feat by wheeling his wife in a wheelbarrow on a rope stretched over the Niagara Falls, while America watched him. Lincoln, watched by America, was on the eve of *his* most tremendous feat; and this is what he said to the onlookers.

'Gentlemen, suppose all the property you were worth was in gold and you had put it in the hands of Blondin to carry across the Niagara river on a rope. Would you shake the cable or keep shouting at him, "Blondin, stand up a little straighter—Blondin, stoop a little more—go a little faster—lean a little more to the North—lean a little more to the South"? No, you would hold your breath as well as your tongue and keep your hands off till he was safe over. The Government is carrying an enormous weight. Untold treasures are in their hands; they are doing the very best they can. Don't badger them. Keep silence, and we will get you safe across.'

APRIL 16
Hannibal Jones Explained

HANNIBAL JONES kept ducks.

APRIL 17
The Cuckoo Comes

THIS is the day
  When cuckoos sing,
And people say
Here comes Spring.
But wise birds stay
With guarding breasts
On Cuckoo-day
To save their nests.

APRIL 18
Cuckoo-Time

I HEARD a little girl talking to herself in bed on a spring
evening. I went into her nursery, and found her sitting up
in her cot cutting out a paper wrist-watch, and murmuring
to herself, 'This is how we do it, you see!' But the paper
bracelet was too short, so she started making a new time-
piece, while I sat on the edge of her bed.

'Will somebody come and put you to sleep?' I asked. She
shook her head. 'Then will you put yourself to sleep?' She
nodded. 'When?' I asked. 'When the clock strikes cuckoo,'
she said.

APRIL 19

'My deare hearte—Plie your book'

O N the 19 of April, 1641, a father imprisoned in the Tower
of London wrote this to his little girl:

'My dearest Nan,

The time, I trust, draws on when I may hope to see you,
which will be one of the best sights I can look upon in this
world. Your father, as you desired, has been hearde speake
for himself, now thes three weekes together, and within a
few days we shall see the conclusion. Ther is, I think, little
fear of my life; soe I hope for a meanes to be left me to let
you see how deare and much esteemed you are and ever
shall be to me.

Look that you learne to play the good housewife, for
now, perchance, there may be need of it; yet, however
fortune befall me, I shall ever willingly give you the first
good of it, and content myself with the second.

My deare hearte,—Plie your book and other learnings,
which will be of use unto you hereafter, and you will see
how we will live happily and contentedly, and live to see
all these stormes blowen over; that so, at leisure, and in
fairer weather, I may tell thee that which I am, and in-
fallibly must be, in all the conditions of life,

Your loving father,

STRAFFORD.'

The Earl of Strafford's hopes did not come true. In May
King Charles the First signed his death-warrant, and the day
his head fell the people built bonfires and danced round them,
while little Nan wept.

APRIL 20
Roast Chicken

ON 20 April 1836 'Jemmy Wood', a rich banker of Gloucester, died. Jemmy was as mean as he was rich. He kept a little boy to do his work; the little boy ate lean, while Jemmy ate fat.

One Sunday morning, as the bells were ringing, Jemmy went to church thinking of the roast chicken he would have for dinner. The little boy stayed at home, to baste the chicken on the spit. The bird turned, the fat sizzled, the chicken-breast browned and glistened. The little boy could not help touching it with the tip of his finger, and putting his finger in his mouth. Oh, how delicious! Suppose he pulled off just a tiny bit of the skin, would it be noticed? Oh, how delicious! Presently—so sharp was his hunger and so small each little theft—the child had left nothing on the spit but the bones.

Now he began to tremble in his shoes. How could he face his master at dinner-time? He crept into a cupboard to hide, and there he saw a bottle, labelled POISON. He heard Jemmy's step outside returning from church, and in his fright thought death would be kinder than a hungry banker. Out came the cork, down went the drink, and the little boy lay senseless on the floor.

Jemmy entered the house primed with thoughts of roast chicken—'But first,' said he to himself, 'a nip of my old brandy, to make it go down better.' And he went to the cupboard chuckling at his own cunning in labelling his fine old brandy POISON, to frighten off the thieves. All he found was an empty bottle, a sleeping child, and nothing but bones for his dinner. There the tale ends. There are several morals in it, if you like to look for them. I'm afraid the little boy found one on his pants, when he woke. But at least he had had his roast chicken.

APRIL 21

What is Time?

WHAT is Time?
   A figment of the mind.
What is Time?
A nothing and a joke.
   What is Time?
More passing than the wind.
   What is Time?
Less than a puff of smoke.
Time is neither After nor Before,
      Time is—
   And is no more.

Roast Chicken

Philip Gough.

APRIL 22
The Value of Time

A LONDON Business-man took a Chinese out to lunch. The Chinese was on a visit to the city, where the rush and press and scurry were something new to him. He was prepared to walk leisurely with his friend to the eating-house, but 'Come along!' cried the Business-man, 'let's go by Tube— we shall save three minutes!' The underground journey was made, and the two found themselves quickly transported to the restaurant. 'Well, here we are in no time!' said the European. 'Yes?' said the Oriental. 'And what do we do with the three minutes we have saved?'

APRIL 23
WILLIAM SHAKESPEARE *born and died* 1564–1616

The First 'Silly Ass'

G OOD people, I have played the beast,
And brought ill things to pass;
I was a man, but thus have made
Myself a silly ass.'

It was all Will Shakespeare's fault. If he had not written *A Midsummer Night's Dream*, Mr. Wilson, the player, would never have acted the part of Nick Bottom at the Bishop of

Lincoln's house in London—and on a Sunday too! The Bishop saw no harm in it; but the Puritans did, and this was in the year 1631, when they were beginning to make themselves felt in Merrie England. So they looked into this scandal; and one Tuesday, from 6 in the morning till 6 at night, Mr. Wilson was condemned to sit in the porter's lodge of the Bishop's house, with his feet in the stocks, an ass's head on his shoulders, a bottle of hay for his dinner, and the verse above pinned on his breast. And everybody who came that day to inquire for my Lord Bishop was answered by an ass.

APRIL 24
Taurus
(*A Zodiac Song*)

LOOK! a lordly Bull,
 Browsing April's grass,
Waiting for Europa
The king's child to pass.
His eye is proud as Jove's,
Godly is his girth,
He bellows for his beauty
Mid the flower-bells of earth.
A garland on his horns
And a posy on his tail,
He'll bear her through the meadows
Like a ship before the gale.

APRIL 25
'Easter-Month'

THE Romans called it Aprilis, the month of Venus, and no month could be more fitly named after the goddess who rose from the foam.

But in England the winds still blew while Italy foamed with flowers; so the Anglo-Saxons called it Oster-Monath, after the easterly gales, and though we have kept the Roman name for April, it is the East Wind which has given its name to the time of Christ's rising from the tomb.

APRIL 26

Everyday Word-Meanings : WINDOW

THIS is a true English word, not planted by a seed from the Latin field, or the Greek, or the French; it sprang in our own Anglo-Saxon, a word that King Alfred would recognize if he heard it. You will find a picture, or metaphor, in this word, if you part it into two: 'wind-ow' means 'wind-eye', an eye is an opening, and window means 'an opening for air'.

In the days when men's dwellings were built of mud and straw there were no cunning chimney-stacks to draw the smoke out of the room, no neat glazed window-frames to let in the light and keep out the wind. But the Anglo-Saxon peasant could not sit in the dark and choke in the smoke, and he poked holes in the roof to let out some of the smoke, and holes in the walls to let in some of the light. Of course, this let in the wind as well, and when it blew hard from any quarter I dare say the goodwife covered the 'wind-eye' on that side of the room with an old cow-hide, or a coarse cloth of her own spinning.

Later on they found out how to put a piece of glass into the wall-holes; the wind now troubled them no more, but the holes were still the eyes of the house, and they kept the old name for them, the word that is our 'window'.

The next time a storm catches your house unawares: when the curtains blow out like sails on a ship, and papers fly all over the room, if your mother doesn't cry 'Shut the wind-eye, quick!' she will cry something very like it.

APRIL 27
A Pointless Tale

Hark to a perfectly pointless tale
That happened last week in a Dorsetshire vale,
When Nelly,
And Katey,
And Peggy the Baby,
Met a very queer fool betwixt sunshine and hail.

Their eyes were like pennies, as round and as brown,
And he asked them their names under Melbury Down.
'I'm Nelly!'
'I'm Katey!'
'She's Peggy the Baby!'
And he gave them three pennies, and went back to town.

Now here's the odd part of this very odd game—
If Nelly, and Katey, and Peggy, by name
Had been Bessy,
And Jessy,
And Tessy the Baby,
This very queer fool would have done just the same!

APRIL 28
A Famous Female Mariner

QUAH-QUAH!' said the Old Grey Goose to her goslings, 'it was on this very day, in seventeen-hundred-and-seventy-two, that she died in the Mile End Road with a silver collar round her neck inscribed by the learned Doctor Johnson himself in good Latin to commemorate her two trips round the globe with Captain Wallis in the *Dolphin* and Captain Cook in the *Endeavour*, for which feats of adventure and endurance the Lords of the Admiralty cried "If ever female deserved to be made an in-pensioner of Greenwich Hospital, this is she!", and signed then and there a warrant to admit her to all its privileges, which the poor dear died too soon to enjoy, and believe it or believe it not, my goslings,' said the Old Grey Goose, 'this notable, much-travelled, much-Latinized much-honoured, Eighteenth-century female mariner was nothing more nor less than a nanny-goat, quah-quah!' (*And it's as true as steel, though I cannot tell you her name.*)

APRIL 29
False April

FALSE April, drest in green,
With cuckoos in her train,
With sunshine and with rain,
    Was here to woo thee.
Ah me! with witching mien
Thy willing heart beguiling,
Now laughing and now smiling,
    Did she undo thee?

Her kisses fly away,
Her yea is turned to nay,
Her love, if not to-day
    It be forgot,
    Will be to-morrow.
Forget, as she forgets,
This fairest of coquettes—
    Believe her not!
Or trust her to your sorrow.

APRIL 30

A Pair of Silk Stockings

April 30th, 1560: From Sir Thomas Gresham in Antwerp,
to Sir William Cecil in London—'I have written into
Spain for silk hose both for you and my lady your wife;
to whom it may please you I may be remembered.'

How Lady Cecil, the wife of the greatest minister of
Queen Elizabeth's reign, must have clapped her hands
over those black silk hose from Spain! How carefully she
must have worn them, to make them last! How she must
have danced in them long after they were darned, and darned,
and darned again! And what those stockings must have cost
Sir Thomas Gresham! Queen Bess herself when a girl hadn't
silk stockings even for Sundays; she wore stockings of cloth,
and her father, King Hal, had *his* hose cut out of 'taffata' one
yard wide, and sewn up.

No girl now thinks twice of having a pair of silk stockings
to her name; many wear silk every day, and throw them in
the rag-bag in a month. But Lady Cecil treasured her Spanish
hose like Spanish gold; *she* never said, 'Good sooth, these have
laddered! Chuck 'em away, Dorcas, and fetch me another
pair.'

MAY

MAY 1

Invitation to Bess

BESSIE, rise and wash your face,
Hat and gown with ribbons lace,
  For the May,
And to fields of Charing come,
Where the merry fiddles hum
  All the day.

There we'll join the jolly souls
Winding mazes round the poles
  Raised on high,
Where the garland overhead
Swings its yellow, white, and red
  Airily.

In a bower set with green
We will curtsey to the Queen
　　As we pass,
In a booth our ease we'll take,
Munching painted ginger-cake
　　On the grass.

If we see at even-close
Ladies dance in silken hose
　　Drinking wine,
Blowing from our ale the froth
We'll dance gay in hose of cloth
　　Half as fine.

Hark! the lusty tabors beat!
Hark! the horns wind, and the sweet
　　Gitterns thrum!
Dress yourself against the day,
And with me to fields of May,
　　Sweet Bess, come.

MAY 2

LEONARDO DA VINCI *died*, 1520

The Painter and the Pig

LEONARDO painted the most famous of all Last Suppers.
He also invented the roasting-spit for his own.
　One day he called for dinner in an inn where the innkeeper
was turning by hand a wooden spit before the fire.
　'Will a roast pig suit your honour?' asked the man.

'Very well,' said the painter.

He sat down and watched the innkeeper continue to turn the spit, while the pig crackled succulently, and the draught drew the smoke up the chimney.

'Heavy work, host.'

'To be sure, sir.'

'And hot work.'

'Indeed, sir.'

'And tedious work.'

'That's true, sir.'

'You might be doing other things.'

'Then who'd roast the pig, sir?'

'The smoke?' suggested the painter.

'That's a good joke,' laughed the host.

The pig was roasted, Leonardo ate his portion, and departed.

After some days he returned with a fan and a set of gears. He fixed the fan in the chimney, and fastened the gears to the spit; the draught drove the fan, the fan turned the gears, and the gears turned the roast before the fire. That is how the automatic spit first started, one of those very simple principles that are so hard to think of.

MAY 3
May's Song

THE moon is on the meadow,
  The nightingale awake,
I have no rest within my breast,
So sweet my heart doth ache.
The blackbird in the garden
Is calling like a bell.
Ah cease! or I of joy shall die,
So full my heart doth swell.
The year's green wave has risen
And broken round my feet—
Oh world of flowers! Oh golden hours!
Oh heart, too full, too sweet!

MAY 4
JOHN JAMES AUDUBON *born*, 1782

The Man who loved Birds

WHAT can one give him for a birthday present?—this ardent ornithologist, who was born in Louisiana, died in New York, and spent half a century travelling over America, to discover, draw, and describe her 1,165 birds. Like England's great field-naturalist, Hudson, he had 'an aquiline style of visage and eye that reminded one of a class of his subjects, a frank, noble, natural man', wrote one who met him in Britain. He crossed the water; but did he ever hear a nightingale sing? America has no nightingales.

Let us give Audubon the nightingale's song for a birthday present.

MAY 5

Listen to the Nightingale!

IT was a German, called Bechstein, who set down on paper the 'words' of the nightingale's song in a way that, to one who knows it, brings it plainer to the ear than almost any musical notation. The one thing I miss among this liquid spilling and trilling of sounds is the long-drawn-out single note which is the strongest call from the tiny singer's heart— a call to whom, and for what, can never be translated.

Here is Herr Bechstein's transcription of all the rest.

Tiouou, tiouou, tiouou, tiouou,
 Shpe tiou tokoua;
  Tio, tio, tio, tio,
Kououtio, kououtiou, kououtiou, koutioutio,
 Tokuo, tskouo, tskouo, tskouo,
Tsii, tsii, tsii, tsii, tsii, tsii, tsii, tsii, tsii, tsii, tsii,
 Kouorror, tiou, tksoua, pipitksouis,
Tso, tso, tso, tso, tso, tso, tso, tso, tso, tso, tso, tso, tsirrhading.
 Tsi, tsi, si, tosi, si, si, si, si, si, si, si, si,
  Tsorre, tsorre, tsorre, tsorreki;
Tsatu, tsatu, tsatu, tsatu, tsatu, tsatu, tsatu, tsatu, tsi,
 Dlo, dlo, dlo, dlo, dlo, dlo, dlo, dlo, dlo,
  Kouiou, trrrrrrrrritzt,
 Lu, lu, lu, ly, ly, ly, li, li, li.

To this I would like to add three long last calls:

Tsuuuuuuuuuuuuuuu!...
Tsuuuuuuuuuuuuuuu!...
Tsuuuuuuuuuuuuuuu!...

MAY 6
Blue Magic

IN the woods the bluebells seem
Like a blue and magic dream,
Blue water, light and air
    Flow among them there.

But the eager girl who pulls
Bluebells up in basketfuls
When she gets them home will find
    The magic left behind.

MAY 7
Don Saltero

'QUAH-QUAH!' said the Old Grey Goose to her goslings,
'it was on this very day in the year Sixteen-hundred-
and-eighty-five that Mr. James Salter was fined Five Pound
Sterling for letting his river-wall fall into ruination, which
sum he lived to retrieve by calling himself Don Saltero and
opening a coffee-and-curiosity-house in Chelsea, where he
who paid for coffee might see for nothing an unrivalled

collection of curiosities, to wit, id est, and videlicet: A Piece of Solomon's Temple—Job's tears that grow on a tree—A curious piece of metal found in the ruins of Troy—A set of beads made of the bones of St. Anthony of Padua—A curious flea-trap—A piece of Queen Catherine's skin—Pontius Pilate's Wife's Great-Grandmother's hat—Manna from Canaan —A cockatrice serpent—The Pope's infallible candle—and last but not least The lance of Captain How Tow Sham, King of the Darien Indians, with which he killed Six Spaniards, and took a tooth out of each head, and put it in his lance as a trophy: which the credulous and the curious came from far and near to see, not excluding that sober man Benjamin Franklin, the Water American himself, which long after the whole bag o' tricks were sold for fifty pound, a mere bagatelle, my goslings,' said the Old Grey Goose, 'if these things were to be believed which of course they were not being nothing but Don Saltero's quah-quah-quah!' (*But that Don Saltero himself is no fabrication you can take from me.*)

MAY 8
Furry-Dance

THE Furry-men in Helston
  To tune of *Hal-on-Tow*
Through the houses of the town
  On May's eighth morning go.
With top-hats on their noddles
  And dress suits on their backs
And lilies in their buttonholes
  The maidens they do tax.

Here a kiss and there a kiss,
    They take their dues, you know,
The day they do the Furry-Dance
    To tune of *Hal-on-Tow*.

MAY 9

FRIEDRICH SCHILLER *died*, 1805

The Lightning

*H*ERR *Gott!* how it thundered that day over Württemberg, in the year of Our Lord, 1766. In the heart of the storm, a little boy rode the branch of a tree, and stared at the sky.

Out of the house ran his mother. 'Friedrich, where art thou? Johann Christoph Friedrich!' A crash sent her hands to her ears. 'Where art thou, Friedrich?'

'Here I am, mother. Up in the tree. Mother——'

'In the tree! *Du lieber Himmel!* come down!'

'Mother! where does the lightning come from?'

'Come down at once! do you want to be killed?'

'But mother, I *must* know where the lightning comes from,' said seven-year-old Schiller.

He was too young to learn, then, where the poet's lightning comes from. But perhaps the child's wondering question inspired the man Schiller to make a play of the legend of Semele, who insisted on beholding Zeus, her lover, arrayed in his lightning; and died of the vision.

[153]

MAY 10

Kingcups in Town

Down the street the old man came,
And on his head he bore a flame.

I stopped to gaze, so he stopped too.
'Want some?' he said. 'Indeed I do.

Where did you get them?' 'Uxbridge way,
All the lot fresh-picked to-day

Off of the island there,' he said,
Shifting the basket from his head.

'You gets 'em when the water's out,
O' course. I had to wait about

All night for 'em. The bud'll bloom
Lovely when they're in your room.'

I took the bunch from him, still wet,
And then the kingcup-gatherer set

His brimming basket on his old
Grey head, and walked beneath the gold,

Yes, walked off in his broken boots,
And the shabbiest of suits,

Crowned in the may-time of the spring,
More gloriously than a king.

MAY 11
The Merchant Adventurers

IT is the 11th of May 1553. The scene is Greenwich, where young King Edward is holding his court.

All Greenwich has turned out to line the Thames; the commoners are as thick as flies on the banks, the courtiers on the terraces gay as peacocks, staid councillors look on from behind the windows, and the palace servants throng the battlements, the first, because they see farthest, to raise the shout of: 'There they come!'

'They' are the first three ships of the Merchant Adventurers, that promising new venture which calls itself:

The Mystery, Company, and Fellowship of the
Merchant Adventurers, for the Discovery of
Unknown Lands.

It has set forth that morning from Deptford, to discover a short cut to China, by some uncharted passage in the North-

East. Sebastian Cabot says there must be one, and though he's too old to go himself, he has laid down the instructions for the voyage. Sir Hugh Willoughby is the general in command, and Richard Chancellor second; and now the three splendid ships sail into sight, the *Bona Esperanza*, the *Bona Confidentia*, the *Edward Bonadventure*.

'Edward! why, where's our King to-day? Not on the terraces or at the windows.'

The young king was sick, too sick to see the show. Perhaps he heard the ships discharge their ordnance—'so that the tops of the hills sounded, and the valleys gave an echo, while the mariners shouted in such sort that the sky rang again.'

But long before the three ships could come home, King Edward died; and of the three two never came home at all, only the *Bonadventure* that bore his name.

MAY 12
The Frozen Ships

THE *Bona Esperanza*,
   The *Bona Confidentia*,
The *Edward Bonadventure*,
   Are gone into the north.
What fortune shall befall them,
   The Merchant Fortune-hunters,
That into unknown regions
   In Maytime sallied forth?

Can they breast the winter,
The icy northern winter,
The Laplander's blind winter
  That England never knows?
The *Bona Esperanza,*
The *Bona Confidentia,*
And both the crews aboard them
  Are turned to frozen snows.

The captain and the seamen,
The merchants and the surgeons,
Man the decks and cabins,
  Seventy, stark and chill;
With frost upon the rigging,
And ice upon the bulwarks
Bitter-cold as iron,
  The lovely ships are still.

MAY 13

A Garland for Agatha Blythe

Here hangs a garland
On a cleft stick,
The four winds of heaven
Round it are met;
When time has withered
The flower that was quick,
The four winds of heaven
Shall sing of it yet:
    Windyfield! Windyfield!
    Never forget.

Here dwells a woman,
Agatha Blythe,
The four winds of heaven
Blow round her cot;
When time has reaped her,
A flower for his scythe,
The four winds of heaven
Shall sing on the spot:
    Agatha! Agatha!
    Never forgot.

MAY 14

'Naebody's Sweetheart's Ugly'

(A Scotch Proverb Tale)

THERE'S a village in Scotland, but I won't tell its name,
where all the lads and lassies were each as bonnie as the
other, and by the grace of God they were just the right age.
By the same grace, there was just the right number of them,
forty fair lassies and forty braw lads—no, I'm wrong! There
was one over, a simpleton who didn't count. If a foreigner
should stop to ask, 'Who's he?' the lad would shrug or the
lassie toss her head—'Him? he's juist naebody.'

Well, one May night when the moon was full they all fell
in love, Jeannie with Jock, Elspeth with Rab, and Mary
with Tammas; and Tammas loved Mary, and Rab loved
Elspeth, and Jock loved Jeannie, so no hearts were broken.
Only Naebody had nobody, but he sat on the pump and
smiled at the moon, quite content.

Then a bit of an argument broke out. Rab, his arm round
Elspeth's waist, was heard to boast, 'Mine's the bonniest
sweetheart in Scotland.' 'That she's not!' swore Jock; and
Tammas swore the same. Soon the lads were at it hammer
and tongs, this one shouting that Meg had the yellowest hair,
and t'other that Janet had the bluest eye; and from praising
their own lassies' looks they went on to run down the looks
of the others, and then it came to fisticuffs. The lassies were
so vexed they could have cried, first to hear themselves called
ugly, and next to see their lads like to spoil each other's beauty.
Off they ran to the manse, crying, 'Meenister! Meenister!
come quick! our lads are spoilin' our faces and their own!'

Out came the Minister, in his spectacles, nightgown, and nightcap. He walked into the midst of the brawl crying, 'Haud yer tongue, Tam! stow yer gab, Rab! peace, ye gowks!' And when he had restored order with a few left-rights, he said severely, 'What's it matter gin Jeannie has the slighter waist and Mary the smaller foot? Dinna ye ken that naebody's sweetheart's ugly? Come awa' tae the kirk, and I'll pair ye all off.'

Which done, the Minister went back to bed, and forty happy couples where they would.

Only the simpleton was left sitting on the pump, sighing as he stared at the moon, 'Naebody's sweetheart's ugly. Naebody's sweetheart's ugly.'

Suddenly he spat at the moon, and she went behind a cloud for shame.

MAY 15
Somebody and Naebody

HAPPY Somebody!
Lucky Somebody!
Somebody's sweetheart's bonnie.
Somebody can't pick an ugly one
Though Somebody's sweethearts are mony.

Poor Naebody!
Pitiful Naebody!
Naebody's sweetheart's dour.
Naebody can't get a bonnie one
Though he pick a year and an hour.

MAY 16
The Virgin Mary's Key-maid

LET's hope that forty pair of sweethearts didn't live to regret it. For of the two things you'd better not do in May, one is to marry. Even Ovid, the poet of love, knew that May weddings are unlucky; he said so hundreds of years ago, and in Latin too.

But you may choose, if not wed, your husband in May; and this is the month when girls in Sweden look for the gold-beetle, whom they call *nyckelpiga*, and whose other name is The Virgin Mary's Key-maid. If they can make her creep over their hands, they say she is giving them their bridal-gloves; and when she flies they follow her with their eyes, north, south, east, or west, for the way she goes is the way the bridegroom will come.

MAY 17
New Clothes and Old

THE other thing not to do in May, of course, is to cast a clout. Change the clothes you wore in April, and you may live to sneeze and regret it. In May, old clothes are kinder to you than new ones.

> I rather like New Clothes,
> They make me feel so fine,
> Yet I am not quite Me,
> The Clothes are not quite mine.
>
> I really love Old Clothes,
> They make me feel so free,
> I know that they are mine,
> For I feel just like Me.

MAY 18
Three Little Princes
(A Mother Goose Rhyme from France)

ON this day Charles Perrault died—and if you've forgotten who *he* was, child (*said the Old Lady*), go back to January and find out. Then you will know why this is a good day for a Mother Goose counting-out rhyme from France.

> Trois petits Princes
> Sortant du Paradis,

La bouche ouverte
Jusqu'à demain midi.
Clarinette! Clarinette!
Mes sabots font des lunettes!
Pêche, pomme, abricot,
Il y'en a une de trop
Dans la cuillère
                    au
                        Pot!

(And just to make it a little clearer)

Three little Princes
Turned out of Paradise,
Mouth hanging open
Expecting something nice.
Isabella! Isabella!
There's a bird in my umbrella!
Peach, plum, apricot,
O what a lot!
There's one too many in
                            the
                                Pot!

(And on POT, of course, 'Out—goes—HE!')

MAY 19

A Tune

I think you'd better have the tune for that one.

MAY 20
'Kemps Morris to Norwiche'

MAY still is, as it always was, the month of Morris-dancing; and the most famous of all Morris-dancers was Will Kemp.

Kemp was an actor; he played in Shakespeare's company, comic parts like Touchstone, Dogberry, and the Gravedigger in *Hamlet*, and he concluded the performances by dancing a 'jigge'. But the greatest dance of his lifetime covered nine days, when, for a wager, he danced every step of the way from London to Norwich. Afterwards he wrote a jolly little book of his adventures on the road:

KEMPS NINE DAIES WONDER
Performed in a Morrice from London to Norwiche.

In it, he nonsensically calls himself 'Cavaliero Kemp, head-master of Morrice-dauncers, high Head-borough of heighs, and onely tricker of your Trill-lilles and Best Bel-shangles', who, 'the first mundaye in Lent began frolickly to foote it' from the Lord Mayor's in London to the Master Mayor's in Norwich.

All along the road people ran out to give him 'bowed (or bent) sixpences or grotes' for luck. At Stratford Bowe they treated him 'with Creame and Cakes'. From Ilford he 'set forward by Moone-shine'. At Chelmsford it took him 'an houre' to reach his 'Inne', because of the crowd of people pressing around him. Outside Chelmsford, a 'Mayde' of fourteen danced for an hour with him along the road. At Sudbury, a lusty tall butcher tried to keep up with him, but fell out after half a mile—'for indeed,' boasts Will Kemp, 'my pace in dauncing is not ordinary'. At Bury, his dance was held up five days by 'a great snow' that fell. From Hingham to Barford-bridge, five young men ran all the way with him. At Norwich, he was met by such a throng, that 'Wifflers' had to clear a way for him to the Market Cross, where the 'Citty Waytes' welcomed him with 'Vyoll and Violin'; and before he reached the Guildhall, where the Mayor was waiting to feast him, Cavaliero Kemp leaped his last leap over the churchyard wall.

So ended the longest non-stop dance of Merrie England.

MAY 21
The day of ST. FELIX
whose flower is

Ragged Robin

RAGGED Robin,
Robin-in-rags,
With your coat-tails
Torn in jags,
Gay as a lark
You sit in the ditch
Having no envy
Of the rich.

[166]

Out-at-elbows
And down-at-heel,
With broken meats
For your midday meal,
A crack in your boot,
A hole in your hat,
A scarecrow's jacket,
Cast-off at that!

Spider shall thread
My needle fine!
I'll mend your jacket
With stitches nine,
I'll darn your stocking,
Your crown I'll thatch,
And on your elbow
Clap a patch.
I'll cook your supper,
I'll brew your tea,
I'll sing with you,
You'll dance with me,
And we'll laugh our fill
While the old world wags,
    I and Robin,
    Jolly young Robin,
    Ragged Robin,
Robin-in-rags!

MAY 22

Pet Marjorie

ON this day, in 1930, a Memorial was unveiled in Scotland
to Sir Walter Scott's 'Pet Marjorie', little Marjorie
Fleming.

Pet Marjorie, wee croodlin dove,
Whom gentle Walter loved above
    All other bairns, whose letters
And rhymes still move our smiles and tears,
This day you're set among your peers,
    Your elders, not your betters.

You were too young to die. But then
You were too young to feel like men,
    Too frail the storms to cherish
Which shook your little passionate
Body with love and fun and hate
    Whereof men seldom perish.

And now within your native land
Reborn in carven shape you stand,
    Since men in reverence dare to
Grant you in stone a second life,
And a far longer one, wee wife,
    Than that God made you heir to.

MAY 23
Gemini
(A Zodiac Song)

GEMINI-JIMINY, Heavenly Twins,
Castor and Pollux as like as two pins,
Born in an eggshell and borne to the blue,
Jiminy-Gemini, how do you do?

MAY 24
CARL LINNAEUS born, 1707

The Man who loved Flowers

CARL LINNÉ, the Swede, gave his life to flowers as Audubon, the American, gave his life to birds. He was born
in south Sweden, on the banks of a beautiful lake, surrounded
by hills and woods and valleys. 'I walked out of my cradle
into a garden,' he said.

His father was a parson, and Carl was to be a parson too;
and because he made no headway in theology was thought
a stupid boy. But people are not stupid where they have
given their hearts, and Carl's was given to flowers. He was
ready to live in poverty and want, if only he might search
for them and study them. His father allowed him eight
pounds a year; Carl stuffed his worn-out shoes with paper,
went without food, and studied botany.

When he was twenty-five he went exploring in Lapland,
sometimes on horseback, sometimes on foot—exploring for
new flowers to bring back to Sweden. He travelled 4,000

miles, discovered 100 unknown plants, and on his return the University presented him with—£10! his travelling expenses. Some years later he found himself in Holland, where a rich Dutch banker gave him the care of his wonderful garden.

This was the sort of paradise Carl had dreamed of; and from here he made excursions to other lands, to bring back ideas and treasures into his Eden. One day in England he fell on his knees, kissed the ground, and prayed. He beheld for the first time a stretch of golden gorse in flower on Putney Heath.

Poor little hungry Carl Linné died at seventy full of honours; his love of flowers, his discoveries, his writings, and the order he created out of chaos in the world of botany, had covered him with glory; and just as flowers have their native names, and their Latin ones as well, *his* simple name was turned into Latin too—and all the world now knows him as Linnaeus.

MAY 25
'Thrice-milking Month'

SOME say the Romans called it *Majores* in honour of the Major Senate of Rome; others say they named it after the lovely Maia, mother of Hermes.

But the Saxons called it Tri-Milchi, the month in which the grass grows so rich that the cows can be milked thrice instead of twice a day.

MAY 26

Everyday Word-Meanings: COW *and* BEEF

WHY do we never say to a guest, 'Will you have some
cow?' but always, 'Will you have some beef?' Why
do we say, 'Have another slice of mutton,' instead of 'Have
another slice of sheep'?

The reason is, that when the Normans conquered England
there were two races living in one land: the Conquerors, who
spoke French, and the Conquered, who spoke Anglo-Saxon.
Now the conquered worked as the servants of the conquerors; and the Anglo-Saxon cowherd in the fields used his
own words, 'cu' and 'oxa', for the cow and the ox he tended.
But when the beast was killed, cooked, and served up in his
master's dining-hall, the French word 'bœuf' was used. It
was always 'beef' and never 'cow' that came to table. And
while the Anglo-Saxon shepherd's 'sceap' bleated on the hills,
it was the French lord's 'mouton' that was roasted for his
supper. So we still talk of a flock of sheep and a leg of
mutton. Our language has kept the Anglo-Saxon names for
the living animals, tended by poor peasants who could speak
no French; and has adopted the French words for the animals

when they were dead, and become meat for Norman noble-men. 'Dead as mutton' has a real meaning in English, for mutton here has never skipped on the hills; the saying has no meaning in France, where 'mouton' is both the living beast and the dead.

This is how scraps of history may get wrapped up in a word. When your father passes his plate and asks for a bit more beef, he is speaking like the French lords of old; and when your mother says, 'Don't let's go into that field, there's a cow in it!' she is talking like the old Saxon peasants.

MAY 27
The Orange Cow

WHEN I walk in the country, I like to have something in my pocket to give an animal. If I have not bread or corn, I offer anything left over from my picnic. Strange horses are easily enticed with apples, pigs with bananas, and hens with cheese. Cats and dogs will mostly come for love; and I have even met a starved-looking goat in Normandy, who at sight of me ran to the end of its tether, rose up, and laid its front legs and head on my shoulders, as starved for love as for food. But cows are kittle cattle, and strange ones, if you draw near, swing their heads sidelong with red sus-picious eyes, and shy away when you hold out your hand.

One spring day in Somerset I leaned on a gate at the top of a steep field where a herd was grazing; and instantly from the bottom of the slope raced an excited heifer, and hung her head by mine over the gate, as friendly as a kitten. I felt that this rare instinctive friendship should get recognition; nothing remained of my lunch but two oranges. I offered one of them to this friendly cow. Rather to my surprise she put forth her broad tongue, licked the fruit into her mouth, chewed it with one big squelch, and swallowed it peel and all, her eyes rolling in ecstasy. I held out the second orange, and she squelched it with the same eagerness. Next day I bought a bag of oranges in Bath, and walked in the same direction as before. As soon as I reached the gate my cow came up at a gallop, waving a large pink tongue. One by one she ate seven oranges for sixpence. I have never found another cow who responded even to the smell of orange-peel. But then, my orange cow was an exception.

MAY 28

THOMAS MOORE *born*, 1780

Tom the Grocer's Son

TOM MOORE, the sweet singer, had a grocer for a father; he kept his shop in Aungier Street in Dublin. When Tom was fifty-five and famous, he went back to visit the house where he was born—'Only think!' he said to his friend Hume, who was with him, 'a grocer's still!' The grocer stood in the door, rather gruff and suspicious, but when the stranger said, 'I am Tom Moore—may I look through the rooms of this house where I was born?' the man's face lit up with a cordial smile; he pulled the poet through the shop into the tiny breakfast-room in the rear, and cried to his wife in a voice that shook with feeling, 'Here's Sir Thomas

[173]

Moore, who was born in this house, come to ask us to let him see the rooms, and it's proud I am to have him under the old roof!'

'He then,' says Tom, 'without delay, and entering at once into my feelings, led me through every part of the house, beginning with the small old yard and its appurtenances, then the little dark kitchen where I used to have my bread and milk in the morning before I went to school; from thence to the front and back drawing-rooms, the former looking more large and respectable than I could have expected, and the latter, with its little closet, where I remember such gay supper-parties, both room and closet fuller than they could well hold, and Joe Kelly and Wesley Doyle singing away together so sweetly. The bedrooms and garrets were next visited, and the only material alteration I observed in them was the removal of the wooden partition by which a little corner was separated off from the back bedroom (in which the two apprentices slept) to form a bedroom for me.' Tom's thoughts and emotions on seeing these things again after five-and-thirty years 'may be more easily conceived than told; and I must say, that if a man had been got up specially to conduct me through such a scene, it could not have been done with more tact, sympathy, and intelligent feeling than it was by this plain and honest grocer'.

On returning to the drawing-room, they found the grocer's wife with a decanter and glasses on the table; and Tom with great pleasure drank her health and her husband's in grocer's port; after which he went to dinner at the Lord-Lieutenant's palace, where he sat at the head of the table and was carved for by an aide-de-camp.

MAY 29
Oak Apple Day

ON Oak Apple Day in Wishford
 The Wiltshire wives will go
To gather green oak in Grovely Wood
 With none to say them no.

Around the streets of Wishford
 With branch and bough they'll go,
Borne from the oaks of Grovely Wood
 Where no man said them no.

And the woodcutting rights in Grovely
 Shall never from Wishford go
While the wives get faggots on Oak Apple Day
 With none to say them no.

MAY 30
MEMORIAL DAY

'Pansies for Thoughts'

THE pansies Ophelia offered were not the pansies we
 know; they were not garden flowers in Shakespeare's
day, and when he put those words in Ophelia's mouth he
was thinking of the small wild heartsease growing in the
Warwickshire meadows. It took a child two hundred years
later to bring them out of the meadows and into the garden.
 One day in May 1810 little Lady Mary Bennet ran with

her basket into the fields to find something to plant in her own garden plot, for she had one to herself in a corner of her father's great garden. She would have heartsease; how many sorts there were! The blue and white and yellow seemed to vary in each. If she could find one of every kind, what a pretty pattern she might arrange on her small plot. Her basket full, she ran back and set to work arranging the variety of colours. Presently a shadow fell on her; her father's clever gardener stood and watched her. He too was struck by the variety and prettiness of the wild flowers, and as he knelt to help her he thought what these wildings might become by cultivation. And out of that day's gardening of the man and the child came pansies as we know them.

MAY 31
Pepys in Vauxhall

'BY water to Fox-Hall,' writes Mr. Pepys in his journal for 1667, as May ran out, 'and there walked in the Spring Gardens. A great deal of company, and the weather and garden pleasant; and it is very cheap going thither, for a man may spend what he will or nothing, all as one. But to hear the nightingale and the birds, and here fiddles and there a harp, and here a jew's trump and there laughing, and there fine people walking, is mighty divertising.'

No doubt Samuel Pepys, with his pleasure in plum-coloured velvets and peach-coloured satins, looked as fine as any. And now May's out, we may all go gay and cast clouts.

Pansies for Thoughts

Philip Gough

M

JUNE

JUNE 1

Out came the Sun!

Out came the sun,
 And out came the dresses!
Girls every one
From tissue recesses
Pulled out the new frock,
The yellow, the pink,
The lavender-blue frock—
And all in a twink
Each one had got on
Her muslin or cotton,
Going all gay on
Gingham and rayon,
Golden as sunlight,
Clear as the sky,
White as the wisp
Of the cloud floating by;

All clean and crisp
They came in the hour
Of the one light
That opens the heart of the flower!
Girls in their summer-gowns
Patterned and plain,
    Girls in green dots
    And rose-coloured spots,
Girls like the rainbow that follows the rain
Brightened the streets of the cities again.

JUNE 2
Whit Monday Peepshow

PEACE and quiet are gone from Hampstead Heath; the showmen have pitched their tents and spread their booths; the paths on the slopes above the Vale of Health are crowded with attractions, the coco-nut shies, the shooting-ranges, the tables where you throw rings to win pink vases and celluloid dolls, the tables where you pitch pennies to gain sixpences, the garish swings where girls toss up and down screaming like parrots, the raucous roundabouts, where children ride on bobbing horses, the crazy arenas where trolleys bump each other, the corkscrew towers where the bold are launched on mats, the sideshows promising shocks or ribaldry, the cheap stalls for toys, finery, and food, the hawkers selling feathers, paper hats, squeaking ticklers, balloons, blue and yellow birds flying on elastic threads, the fortune-tellers and the fortune-seekers, the gilt caravans drawn to the back of the scene, where something is always cooking and brewing,

[179]

the lost child wailing and weeping for its parent, the paper-bag picnickers spread far and wide, the trail of paper and peel, the dogs, the sweethearts, the promenaders looking on from afar at a scene reduced to a haze and sounds reduced to a hum, and beyond them the rich untroubled grass, the golden gorse-pits and the white birch-groves, the squirrels, and the skylarks, and the sky.

JUNE 3

June's Song

I BRING you my rose.
It is a golden flame.
Is Love its name?
It is a scarlet fire.
Is it desire?
'Tis the white ash of coal.
Is it the soul?
One, none, or all of those,
I bring you my rose.

JUNE 4

DERBY DAY

So here's a song for the swiftest horse of all.

Pegasus

FROM the blood of Medusa
Pegasus sprang.
His hoof upon heaven
Like melody rang,
His whinny was sweeter
Than Orpheus' lyre,
The wing on his shoulder
Was brighter than fire.

His tail was a fountain,
His nostrils were caves,
His mane and his forelock
Were musical waves,
He neighed like a trumpet,
He cooed like a dove,
He was stronger than terror
And swifter than love.

[181]

He could not be captured,
He could not be bought,
His running was rhythm,
His standing was thought;
With one eye on sorrow
And one eye on mirth,
He galloped in heaven
And gambolled on earth.

And only the poet
With wings to his brain
Can mount him and ride him
Without any rein,
The stallion of heaven,
The steed of the skies,
The horse of the singer
Who sings as he flies.

JUNE 5
'You cannot tell'

TALKING of horses, I heard this tale told in an after-
dinner speech by a Chinese Ambassador; it was, he said,
a well-known tale in China, but it was new to me, and I
thought it was worth remembering, for it is as wise a tale in
the West as in the East.

One day a farmer found his stable-door open, and his
only horse gone. Hearing of his loss, his friends came to
commiserate. 'Oh!' they cried. 'What a calamity!' The

farmer, who was a philosopher, replied, 'You cannot tell. It may prove to be a blessing.'

The following day the horse returned, bringing with him a fine mare. Once more the farmer's friends flocked about him. 'You have now two horses instead of one,' they cried. 'What a blessing!' The farmer said, 'You cannot tell. It may prove to be a calamity.'

The following day the farmer's son rode the new mare; but she was too lively for him; she threw him, and the young man's leg was broken. 'Alas!' cried the farmer's friends. 'What a calamity!' 'You cannot tell,' said the farmer; 'it may be a blessing.'

The following day a war broke out in that part of China; all the young men of the village joined the army, and were killed in battle. All, that is, but the farmer's son, who could not fight because of his broken leg, and lived to farm his father's lands in peace.

Thus you see how many a blessing may give rise to a misfortune, and out of many a misfortune a blessing may spring.

JUNE 6

Two Odd Americans

DR. GATEWOOD of Chicago, and Mr. William Perry of Audubon, both died in June 1938. Dr. Gatewood was 51, Mr. Perry was 86; they had nothing to do with one another, but there was something odd about each of them.

Dr. Gatewood never had a Christian name. His parents were unable to agree on one they liked, and decided to wait and let him choose his own. And he never did.

William Perry said nothing for fifty years. He wasn't dumb. But on his wedding-day, when his bride jilted him, he vowed at the altar not to speak a word till she came back; which *she* never did. And he kept his word.

JUNE 7

The day of the DUNMOW FLITCH

Flitch of Bacon

DARBY and Joan, to Dunmow go,
To win the Flitch of Bacon.
First you twain must fairly show
The year has passed without a blow,
An angry word or scowling face—
And if you twain can prove your case,
Then home the Flitch is taken.
But if the Counsel prove you wrong,
Or if a Witness come along
To swear that Darby browbeat Joan
Or Joan employed the henpeck's tone,
Then home you go without the Flitch—
For only wedded couples which
Can keep the household peace like friends
In betwixt a twelvemonth's ends,
Can hope to save their Bacon.

JUNE 8

The Quack of Quacks

WAY there! for Count Cagliostro in his coach-and-four, driving all over Europe selling love-philtres, beauty-potions, charms, and the Elixir of Youth! Why, he can change hemp into silk, and other wonders!

(*Hush! Count Cagliostro is really Joseph Balsamo, the son of a poor shopkeeper in Palermo, where he began life by forging a will, counterfeiting theatre-tickets, robbing his uncle, and swindling a goldsmith.*)

Way there! for the Countess Seraphina, Cagliostro's beautiful wife. She looks as young as sweet-and-twenty, but swears she's not a day under sixty, ladies! How? Because she has tested for herself the Count's Elixir of Youth.

(*Hush! her parents are girdle-makers in Rome, her name is Lorenza, and if you want the truth, she's no older than she looks.*)

No wonder that the Aristocracy, nay even Royalty, pay fabulous prices for a small phial of the miraculous Elixir. Who doesn't want to be young and beautiful for ever? Even the Cardinal de Rohan is his dupe.

What a goldmine Joseph Balsamo became for the romancers. The arch-romancer, Alexander Dumas, made him the centre of some of his best novels, and presented Cagliostro as a real magician, and even a profound and noble character. But when you have read 'The Memoirs of

[185]

a Physician', it may amuse you to turn to Carlyle's *French Revolution*, and find Cagliostro described as:

'Healer of diseases, abolisher of wrinkles, friend of the poor and impotent, grand master of the Egyptian mason-lodge of high science, spirit-summoner, gold-cook, grand cophta, prophet, priest, and thaumaturgic moralist and swindler; really a liar of the first magnitude, thoroughpaced in all provinces of lying, what one may call the king of liars.'

And the Quack of quacks.

JUNE 9

May-Day in June

ON Shillingstone Green
A Maypole towers.
On June the Ninth
They dress it with flowers,
And do their dance
And sing their tune
And keep May-Day
On the Ninth of June.

The wreaths are left
Until they are brown,
The pole stands up
Until it falls down,
And why these Dorsetshire
Folk do so
Never ask me
For I don't know.

Cagliostro
BORN 1743

Philip Gough

JUNE 10
Gold-Weed

THEY called my buttercup a weed
And told me, 'Pull it up!'
I let it stand and flower and seed,
My golden buttercup.

Next year when it was twice its size,
'Root out that weed!' they said.
I let it stand and spread and rise
And seed upon its bed.

In the third year when it came up
My gold weed was a bower,
And when they saw my buttercup,
They cried out, '*What* a flower!'

JUNE 11
A Golden Legend

ROUND about the time William of Normandy was making 1066 one of the famous dates in history, there was a boy in France called Gerbert, who became a monk in Fleury, then Archbishop of Rheims, and finally the Pope. He had the reputation of being a magician, perhaps because he had found out how to work an organ with hot water, and quick-witted folk were suspected by the slow-witted then more than now. This tale is told of his wits, when he was in Rome, and how much you choose to believe of it is your affair and nobody else's.

In the Campus Martius stood a statue with outstretched forefinger; on its head were written the words: *Strike here*! Gerbert was told that the statue indicated a hidden treasure, and many treasure-seekers had struck the figure on the head, thinking it concealed gold or gems; but the statue had been mutilated in vain. Gerbert thought differently; he considered the outstretched finger, noted where its shadow struck the ground at noon, marked the spot, and came back at midnight, with his lantern-bearer. He opened up the ground (some say by magic arts), and laid bare a noble entrance into a golden palace: walls, roof and floor, pillars, seats and tables, all were of gold; a golden king and a golden queen sat served with golden food on golden plates; the servants behind them bore golden dishes and ewers; golden soldiers were gambling with golden dice; a golden dog crouched over a golden bone. All was lit by a small but rare carbuncle, so pure that it filled the hall with light; in a far corner stood a golden boy, his golden arrow drawn to the head on his bent bow. Gerbert stretched out his hand to touch a vessel of golden grapes, and as he did so it seemed to him that all the gold images were about to rise and rush on him. Wisely, he held his hand; but his lantern-bearer, less wise, picked up a gold knife from the table. Suddenly the hall was filled with clamour, as soldiers and servants sprang to their feet; at the same moment, the boy let fly his shaft; it struck the carbuncle and the light went out. 'Throw down the knife!' cried Gerbert; his man obeyed; and turning their backs on the black cavern, they fled by lantern-light up into moonlit Rome. The entrance closed behind them, and no man has found it since.

JUNE 12

The Golden Touch

KING MIDAS had the Golden Touch,
It gave King Midas' finger such
Surprising power that if he brushed
A singing-bird its song was hushed,
Imprisoned in a lump of ore
That looked, but was, a bird no more.
The child that in unvalued bloom
Ran to meet him in the room,
At Midas' kiss gleamed hard and cold,
Worth nothing but her price in gold.
The rose he plucked weighed down his hand,
The pear he bit grew solid and
Jarred on his teeth and gave no juice.
What was the use, what *was* the use
To Midas of his Golden Touch?
I do not envy Midas much.

Man's magic fails. But when the God
Of Light from heaven gives a nod,

The bird's brown breast as gold is bright,
And all his singing runs like light;
The bare-limbed children on the shore
Lose their pallor evermore,
Becoming where the Touch doth fall
Like apricots on summer's wall;
The rose among her foliage glows.
And double fragrance from her flows,
The ripe pear glistens in the sun,
And twice as sweet its juices run.
Alas for men who use the power
Of gold on bird, child, fruit, or flower—
Only the gods, who know so much,
Know how to use the Golden Touch.

JUNE 13
'Little Canada'

ONE day in June 1604 the Dauphin of France pushed
away his cherries.

'Eat them up,' said Dr. Jean Héroard, his physician-in-
charge. 'They're nice. They'll do you good.'

The Dauphin, not yet three years old, shook his head.
'That's for Canada,' he said.

He had seen the Indian child they called Canada go by,
looking sick and sorry. Poor little Canada! A year ago
M. de Champlain had gone on a voyage of discovery to the
big strange country found and abandoned by old Jacques
Cartier, and had lived among a wild tribe of redskins they
called Hurons. When M. de Champlain came back he

brought a small Huron with him, to be the pet of the French Court; and he was known as little Canada, after the big land he came out of. But you cannot transplant the Red Indian. All through spring and summer the child wilted, and wrung the Dauphin's heart with pity. Dr. Héroard, who watched the prince as the apple of his eye, wrote this in his journal: 'The Dauphin watched little Canada go by, ill. Sent him his soup.' And later: 'At half past eleven had his dinner. He gave a bowl of cherries a push saying, "That's for Canada".'

The Dauphin grew up to be one of France's weak kings; his father, Henry of Navarre, and his son, Louis XIV, out-shone him in glory. But perhaps that movement of compassion, set down by Dr. Héroard, tells something of him that history hasn't recorded; although Canada never got that bowl of cherries. When it was brought to him, he was already in the Hurons' happy hunting-ground.

JUNE 14
'Junior Month'

THE Romans had two names for it: Juno-Month, which the poet Ovid gave it, as belonging to the Queen of the goddesses, and Junioribus, by which the fourth month of the Roman calendar was dedicated to the Junior branch of the Roman legislature, as May was dedicated to the Major branch.

But what the Anglo-Saxons called it does not seem to be on record—a pity, for their names, drawn straight from the earth and the season, seem to me to have the best roots and the sweetest sounds.

JUNE 15

The Nile and the Lady

IF the Nile is doing his duty, he begins to-day to rise between his banks for the great annual overflow which saves Egypt from the drought. Most lands whose crops are threatened by summer heat hope for water to fall from heaven; in Egypt they pray for water to rise from the earth. For these favours, Egypt of old looked on the Nile as a god; and if their god delayed his favours by a single day, they offered him a sacrifice to bring him round. On June the Fifteenth, the day when he must stir, the loveliest girls in Egypt watched him anxiously, wishing, for the first time in their lives, that they were less lovely; for what could a god be given but the most beautiful woman in the land? It was small consolation that she would be dressed in the richest robes. Or did the lady, a thousand years ago, feel an exalted joy in her silks and gold and garlands, when she was brought to the banks of the Nile and flung to the embrace of the sluggish god? She may have done. But as ideas grew less barbarous with the times, and human sacrifice was replaced by a written prayer, the mothers of fair daughters must have rejoiced the first year in which a letter instead of a lady was thrown into the Nile.

JUNE 16

Kate Greenaway's Number

UNTIL the month of June, 1764, the houses in a street
were never numbered. Before that, shops and lodging-
houses, as well as inns, were known by their signs, stuck
against the walls or hung in air: a big gilt half-moon, a
painted coat, a grape-crowned Cupid straddling a small
barrel. A traveller might lodge at 'the Sygne of the Dogges
Hed in the Pot', buy silk for his wife at 'the Sygne of the
Angell in Cheapside', or Shakespeare's sonnets for himself at
'the Sygne of the Cocke in Paul's Churchyard'. You must
go by the signs to find a certain person in a certain street.
And then, like a great revolution, the numbers came in, and
it was as easy as one-two-three to find Mr. So-and-so's house
or shop. New Burlington Street began it; Lincoln's Inn
Fields caught on; and the novelty spread like a fashion or a
fever. The old signs stayed until they crumbled away; but
nobody tried to renew them. With luck you may still find
one here and there, the gilt tarnished, the paint washed off,
the wood worm-eaten, the plaster broken; but the signs
were beaten by the numbers for good and all, that June.

More than a hundred years later, Miss Kate Greenaway,
that maker of sweet picture-books, came to live in Frognal
fields, bordering Hampstead. Her house was the only one
in the lane, and she thought she would have a name for it,
for people had begun to colour their houses again with words.
But she was told that though she *might* choose a name for her
house, she *must* have a number. 'Well,' said demure Miss
Greenaway, 'I suppose I may choose my number'—and her

house-all-alone became known as No. 50, Frognal. For some years it defied the authorities; but presently houses began to appear on each side of it, and when the country lane became a street, Miss Greenaway's home sank somewhere among the thirties. The numbers wouldn't stand Kate's pretty nonsense; they won again.

JUNE 17

The Battle of Bunker Hill, 1775

T'other Side of Duck-Pond

T'OTHER side of Duck-Pond
 When the month is young
Hark at Yankee Doodle
With his sassy tongue.
'Hip, Georgie Washington!
Hip with a will!
Who chased the Britisher
All round Bunker Hill?
Ho, Georgie Hanover,
Georgie Number Three!
Who lost Ameriky
For a Cup o' Tea?'

JUNE 18

The Peacock and the Nightingale

(A Serbian Proverb Tale)

IN June, the month of weddings-after-May, Madam Peahen and Mrs. Nightingale met and compared notes.

'How did you choose yours, madam?' asked the little bird
of the big.

'By eye, my dear! I may say by a hundred eyes. For when
he stood before me and opened his tail, I was caught like a fly
in a web of sapphires and emeralds. It was quite irresistible
in the sun on the castle wall.'

'And how is it in the home?'

'Screech, screech, screech!' said the Peahen. 'When he
says Come here, Go there, Do this, or Don't do that, it's one
perpetual headache. I married him for his beauty, but I've
come to learn that beauty is only plume-deep. Haven't you,
Mrs. Nightingale?'

'Dear Madam Peahen! I never even set eyes on my little
man, when he began courting. But I heard him calling
through the dark, and my heart went out to him through
my ear.'

'And how has it answered?'

'Oh, sweet, sweet, sweet!' said she. She added, modestly,
'He isn't much to look at, you know.'

And the owl in the church-tower, who had seen more
weddings than most, said, 'Marry by the ear and not by
the eye.'

JUNE 19

Plain Philomel

PROUD Peacock glitters in the sun,
Plain Philomel is drest in dun.

Proud Peacock has a jewelled coat,
Plain Philomel a honied throat.

Proud Peacock's song is music's knell.
I will wed plain Philomel.

JUNE 20

The Reindeer

ONE June, a few years ago, Mr. Rasmus Rasmussen came
to London. It was no joy to him to come; he missed
the ice and the silence of his native Lapland, this small fair
man in his gay pull-over, his leather leggings, and his shoes of
grass. With the reindeer knife in his belt and ribbons round
his ankles he was only one of the strange sights in London,
but everything in London was strange to him. So he went to
the one place where he knew he would find his friends.

Before he left England he was asked what he would
remember longest of the new things he had seen. He said,
'The imprisoned reindeer in the Zoo. Naturally I love
reindeer. They are my best friends. They understand me
as well as I understand them. I spoke to that one—you might
say in the reindeer language. The animal turned to me as if

[197]

to say "Take me away from this life. I don't want to live in London. Take me back to Lapland." I felt like whipping out my knife, and ending my friend's misery.'

JUNE 21
Golden Jubilee

I CAN just remember the Golden Jubilee of Queen Victoria, on 21 June, 1887. I was much too little to see it, but I remember the excitement in the air that summer, and I remember how I and my brothers made gold-paper crowns in which we marched round the garden, holding very upright thin gold sticks for sceptres. They were really the wooden sticks with which my father staked our flowers, and we had pasted them with strips of gold paper, which fell into loose spirals after they had been gripped in our sticky fists. And I remember a little friend who came to see us, and *would* be Queen Victoria in that Golden Jubilee Procession round the gravel paths; and because she was a guest we had to let her be, though I secretly longed to be Queen Victoria myself, and so did my brothers.

My father and mother saw the Three Processions which went in front of Queen Victoria's carriage drawn by eight cream-coloured ponies.

In the First Procession rode the Indian Princes and their Suites, followed by the Queen of Hawaii and her Attendants in Gold Cloth.

In the Second Procession, fifteen carriages 'each horsed

with four bays', full of Kings and Queens, Crown Princes and Grand Dukes.

In the Third Procession, which was the Queen's, she had a Guard of Honour of six Royal Princes; one was the Prince of Wales (who became Edward the Seventh), and one the Crown Prince of Germany (the ex-Kaiser Wilhelm). And then came

THE QUEEN

with her cream-coloured ponies, followed by a bevy of Dukes and Princes.

All this was printed on my parents' official programme, which I still have. It sounds very splendid—*almost* as splendid as the Golden Procession of myself, my three brothers, and little Marie Barnes, round the back-garden gravel-paths in Adelaide Road.

JUNE 22

Cancer

(*A Zodiac Song*)

OVER the beaches of the sky
The Crab no fisherman has caught
Ambles his clumsy course in June.

The silver shells of stars unsought
By mariners and children lie
About his sidelong journey strewn.

Heaven's bed lies high and dry.
Old Shellback with a single thought
Clambering up the hot blue dune

Sees and thinks and wishes naught
In night's dark aridity
But the clear pool of the moon.

JUNE 23

The First Regatta

THE first regatta held in England took place on 23 June,
1775. Lady Montague, who had visited Venice, returned with glowing descriptions of a Water-Fête she had
seen on the Grand Canal. Italy, land of sunshine and blue
skies, of singing and laughter, has always known how to
make carnival; and the gay scene on the water, the gondola
races, the feasting and dancing, the lights and the mandolines,
enchanted the great lady. When she had told her story,
London cried, 'We also have a river! let us have a regatta
too.' For this festival on the Thames they kept the Italian
name *Rigatta*; *Riga*, the Italian word for a row, represented
the line of boats drawn up at the start of a race.

English summer skies are as often grey as blue; and after
wonderful preparations, the First Regatta had to be put off
again and again. That was the sort of summer it was in
1775. But at last the weather grew kinder, and on Midsummer Eve the Regatta took place.

The City Companies lent their gorgeous barges for the occasion, and all the rowers in the races wore one of the marine colours, red, white, or blue. The White Oarsmen were placed in the middle of the river, against the centre arch of Westminster Bridge, the Red Oarsmen were drawn up on the Surrey side, and the Blue Oarsmen on the Middlesex bank. From London Bridge to Millbank the river was crowded with pleasure boats; people who could not sit in the Guild Barges paid half-a-guinea for a seat in a coal-barge. Boats full of refreshments plied their oar and their trade, twenty-one cannons went off when the Lord Mayor arrived, gaming-tables were set up on all the roads leading to Westminster Bridge, and its arches were turned into concert-rooms.

At seven in the evening, after the races, a procession headed by the Red, White, and Blue Watermen was followed up the river by 200,000 folk in other boats; it took them two hours to reach Ranelagh, where a 'Temple of Neptune' had been erected in the gardens. The Temple was an octagon lined with strips of red, white, and blue; between the eight supporting pillars eight lustres sparkled. The merry-makers landed from the water, and mingled with swarms of parties on the banks; and here they supped and danced till Midsummer morning. So ended the first English regatta.

MIDSUMMER DAY

Midsummer Maids

S UE, Lou, and Prue met on Midsummer Day.
'Good morning, Sue!'
'Good morning, Lou!'
'Good morning, Prue!'
'Did you?'
'*Did* you?'
'Did *you?*'

Sue said: '*I* sowed hemp-seed. At midnight to the minute I sowed it in our back-yard, and said the charm without a single slip: *Hemp-seed I sow, hemp-seed I hoe, and he that is my true love come after me and mow!* Then—I looked behind me!'
'Did you see?'
'Who was he?'
But Sue wouldn't tell.

Lou said: '*I* damped my shift. At midnight to the minute I took a clean one from my drawer, dipped it in water, turned it inside out, and hung it over a chair-back in front of the fire. Then—I listened for his step to come and turn it outside in.'
'Did you hear?'
'Was he near?'
But Lou kept her mouth shut.

Prue said: 'The hemp-seed is good, and the wet shift is good, but *I* believe in the rose. At midnight to the minute I walked backward into the garden and gathered the sweetest rose on the red rose-tree, and I never said a word, but put it

between white paper, and if I don't look till Christmas it will
be as fresh as now, and I'll wear it in my bosom and he'll
come and take it out.'
'Will he, Prue?'
'Yes, but who?'
But Prue smiled and said nothing.
So silly are maids at Midsummer.

JUNE 25

ST. ERASMUS DAY
(Whose flower is the Pimpernel)

Open Eye, Pimpernel

O PEN eye, Pimpernel, chin-in-the-dust!
Sun in the heavens is yellow as rust.
Shut your eye, Pimpernel, chin-in-the-dew!
Rain from the heavens is come to drown you.

JUNE 26

Mind Your Manners!

Y OU are a little French boy, or a little French girl, please.
King Henry the Fourth who sits on the throne of France,
King James the First, who wears the crown in England, have
forks to eat with at table. But these new, amusing, two-
pronged things are not for children; their fingers are still
quite good enough for *them*, as they were for their fathers
and mothers. But even about fingers, there are manners.
'François! Françoise!' cries Nurse. 'How often must I

tell you only to use *three* fingers when you take your portion from the dish? You're using all five, you naughty little thing!'

'François! don't cram your food in your mouth with *both* hands! one hand at a time, *if* you please—you're not a monkey. Françoise! don't dig your egg out of its shell with your thumb—no, no, child! don't lick it out with your tongue, either! Use the sippet of bread I've cut you. And François! smear your cheese on your bread with a knife, and stop buttering it with your fingers and thumb this instant! Yes, I know your silver bowl will be brought round soon for you to dip in but there's manners *at* dinner as well as after it, and it's my part to see you behave like little ladies and gentlemen.'

JUNE 27
Everyday Word-Meanings: PLATE—BOWL

IF at dinner Aunt Hezekiah said, 'Pass up your flat for some pudding, Sam!'—or if Sam should demand, 'More water, Aunty! my round's empty'—you might take it for a good joke, and laugh, or for a bad one, and tell the joker not to try to be funny. The funny thing is, the joker would be very near the truth.

The word 'Plate' is really the same word as 'Flat', and if you say it aloud it even *sounds* flat. Wherever the French word *Plat* has worked its way into our language it carries a flat meaning: a Platter is a flat dish or tray, a Plateau is flat table-land, a Platform is a flat surface, and a Platitude a flat remark. 'Plate' meant, and still means, a thin sheet of metal;

and long before the days of china and earthenware, silver and gold 'plate' was used at table by the rich folk, while the poor folk ate their food off wooden trenchers, or even off 'plates' of bread. When they had eaten the meat off the bread, they ate up the 'plate' itself.

Then, Bowl. Before drinking-glasses took their present shape, the poor man's drinking-vessel was a wooden bowl. The Anglo-Saxon word for it was Bolla, which sounds nearly the same as the French word 'Boule' for a ball, or the Latin 'Bolus' for a pill. Say it aloud, and you'll see how *round* it sounds; and then notice the roundness of many things which sound like it—of Bulbs, and Bulges, and Bullets, and Bales, and the Bole of a tree, and the Bulk of a body.

This seems to lead us a long way from the Bowl we began with, but they all belong to the same family party. Remember at *your* next family party that you eat off the Flat and drink out of the Round.

JUNE 28
The Baronet's Bet

'QUAH-QUAH!' said the Old Grey Goose to her Goslings, 'men will bet anything for the sport of it, but I'll bet you never heard of a bet like Sir John Throckmorton's, the Berkshire Baronet who, being in gaming company in June 1811, wagered a thousand guineas that at eight o'clock in the evening he would dine in a well-woven, well-dyed, well-made suit of wool which at five o'clock in the morning had been fleece on the backs of two sheep, to which some fool, taking Sir John for a fool, cried *Done!* whereon Sir John called on Mr. Coxetter of Greenham Mills and laid the case before him, and Mr. Coxetter, who knew his business, provided sheep and shearers and washers and carders and stubbers and rovers and spinners and weavers and dyers, with a master-tailor to end with, and without a second to lose at five a.m. on the 28th of June, the sheep were shorn, the fleece was washed, the wool was carded, stubbed, roved, spun and woven into cloth, the cloth was scoured, fulled, tented, raised, sheared, dyed, and dressed, and the tailor set to with tape-measure, shears, buttons and needle and thread, and believe it or not, my goslings,' said the Old Grey Goose, 'that very same evening Sir John Throckmorton entertained his guests at dinner in a handsome damson suit, with a thousand guineas in his pocket and an hour and three-quarters to spare.' (*And I wager a thousand farthings this is true.*)

JUNE 29

ST. PETER'S DAY

The Rush-Strewing

ONE winter night, long ago, a woman was lost among the fields near Aylesbury. It was dark and cold, and there was nobody near. How could she find her way? If she did not, what would be the end of it? Her body was numb and her heart was chilled with fear. Then she heard church-bells ringing, somewhere or other, and guided by the sound, she came to a place called Wingrave. It was in the days when the floors of houses, man's and God's, were strewn with rushes.

The woman lost in the fields owned fields of her own. When she died, it was found she had left one of them for ever to the Parish of Wingrave, to pay for the strewing of new rushes on the church floor. The day for the strewing was St. Peter's Day, if it fell on a Sunday, and if not, for the first Sunday after St. Peter's. The bells had saved her in winter, but no doubt she chose a summer day for the rush-strewing, when the rushes would be at their greenest. The custom has not died, but now it is grass, not rushes, they strew in the church, to keep her gratitude green.

JUNE 30

A Thirteenth-Century Farmer Makes His Will

AND talking of old wills, here's how one was made by a farmer, called Reginald Labbe, who died in 1293. At that time wills had to be written in Latin, and Reginald Labbe could neither write nor read, much less speak the Latin tongue. So to the parish clerk he betook himself.

THE CLERK: How much money have you to leave?

LABBE: Not one penny. I have a cow and a calf, two sheep, three lambs, as many hens, a bushel and a half of wheat, a seam and a half of fodder, a seam of barley, another of mixed grain, and one halfpenny-worth of salt. Besides these, I own, in clothes, a tabard, a tunic, and a hood; my household goods are a rug, a bolster, two sheets, a brass dish, and a trivet.

THE CLERK: You're well off. How do you wish to leave these

things? And pray remember that, as you have no money, some of them must be sold to defray expenses.

LABBE: What do you reckon they're worth?

THE CLERK: Thirty-three shillings and eightpence all told.

LABBE: And what will the expenses come to?

THE CLERK: A penny to dig your grave and twopence to toll the bell. Then there will be eightpence to prove this will, and six shillings for bread-and-cheese for your mourners. And, say, another crown for fees of other sorts.

LABBE: Those figures are beyond me. But when all is paid, I should like to make these bequests. A sheep to the church in Newton, and another to the altar-and-fabric fund at Oakwood. To my wife Ida, or rather, to Ida my widow, one-half of my cow, and to Thomas Fitz-Norreys a quarter of my calf.

THE CLERK: Is that all?

REGINALD: I can't think of anything more.

THE CLERK: That will be sixpence for the making of the will, and threepence more for the writing of it out.

REGINALD: I can't pay you now, but I will when I'm dead. The sheep are worth tenpence apiece—take one for your trouble.

THE CLERK: That will do very well.

The Clerk then wrote it all down, and Reginald Labbe went home with peace in his mind, and a Latin will in his pocket.

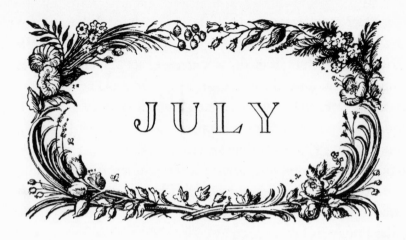

JULY

JULY 1

Who's that Bleating

WHO'S that bleating
Down by river?
Sheep are sweating,
Soon they'll shiver.
Back to farm
Without their wool,
We'll go warm
And they'll go cool.

JULY 2

Beans and Bacon

DANIEL DAY, a pump-and-block maker of Wapping, was
such an excellent man that he was known to his friends
as 'Good Day'. He owned and enjoyed a little country place

o

[209]

near Fairlop in Essex, and wandering in Hainault Forest hard by had come to love a superb oak-tree that grew there. Its trunk was 33 feet in girth, seventeen of its branches were as big apiece as an ordinary oak-tree, and it was known as the Fairlop Oak. This was in the eighteenth century.

On a day in July, which happened to be the first Friday in the month, 'Good Day' had a fancy to dine under the huge and noble boughs, and invited a few chosen friends to join him there and partake of beans and bacon. The rustic feast was so successful that Good Day decided to repeat it on the first Friday in July as long as he lived.

The custom became known in the neighbourhood; others began to mark the day by eating a dinner of beans and bacon under the Fairlop Oak. In a few years the numbers grew so great that vendors of refreshments came along to sell food to the crowds; these, in another year, were followed by hawkers of knick-knacks and trifles; next year came the travelling peep-shows and conjurors. In short, Good Day's simple dinner swelled into a huge annual fair, whose chief visitors were the pump-and-block makers of Wapping. They came forty strong in a wooden boat on wheels, drawn by six horses, with a band of music inside and an awning overhead. So now every year nearly half a hundred Wapping pump-and-block makers ate their beans-and-bacon under Fairlop Oak, where at first only one ate them.

Good Day lived to a ripe old age, full of kindness and crotchets. He never married, but looked after his sister's children as his own, and went daily to his gate to relieve the poor who gathered there. He liked neither horses nor tea; but he was served by an old widow who loved tea only second to her wedding-ring, and when she died Good Day had her buried with her ring on her finger and a pound of tea in each hand. For himself he would have no other coffin than one of the great boughs of the Fairlop Oak, after it had fallen by some accident. It was fashioned to his size, and to make sure it was the *right* size he lay down in it, and had himself conveyed to Barking churchyard by water, preferring boats to horses. At Barking Good Day got out of his coffin and, let us hope, did not return to it for many another day. One grief his death spared him; he did not live to see his well-loved tree largely destroyed by fire in 1805.

JULY 3
Fairlop Friday

WHEN oak has got his summer cloak
What jolly thoughts awaken
Of Friday Feasts at Fairlop Oak
Where men eat beans-and-bacon.
'Good day to you! good day to you!'
The Wapping diners say—
'We drink to you, and say to you
'Good day to you, Good Day!'

JULY 4
Independence Day, 1776

THE author of America's Declaration of Independence was her third president, Thomas Jefferson. On his eightieth birthday, Jefferson wrote to John Adams, America's second President:

'I have ever dreaded a doting age; and my health has been generally so good, and is now so good, that I dread it still. The rapid decline of my strength during the last winter, has made me hope sometimes that I see land. During summer I enjoy its temperature; but I shudder at the approach of winter, and wish I could sleep through it with the dormouse, and only wake with him in the spring, if ever. I am told you walk well and firmly. I can only reach my garden, and that with sensible fatigue. I ride, however, daily, but reading is my delight.—God bless you, and give you health, strength, good spirits, and as much life as you think worth having.'

In three more years, Thomas Jefferson 'saw land'. He died on the fiftieth anniversary of the great day he had helped to bring about; the day when his famous Declaration is read again to the nation, and when from every fort and battle-ship salutes are fired at sunrise, noon, and sunset. With those sounds in his heart, if not in his ears, the Third President died; and on the same day, to the same sounds, died John Adams.

JULY 5
'Most Gratifying!'

'REALLY, it is beautiful! most gratifying!' said Queen Victoria on 5 July 1847, as she stepped out of the train at Cambridge. The young Queen was wearing a white

Most Gratifying

bonnet and a dress of peach-coloured satin, and the Royal carriage was decorated in white and gold. The Prince Consort was with her, more reserved but no less moved than she; for on this day they had travelled for the first time by special train. George Hudson, 'the Railway Napoleon', received her on the platform; he opened the railway-carriage door himself, and she walked on his arm down the platform to a little pavilion. It was the moment of his lifetime for this Yorkshire farm-boy turned railway-king, who talked with a broad burr, and whose daughter, although he was a millionaire, was cut by the titled young ladies at her school. Ah! if they could see the lass's father now, with the Earl Marshal walking before him, and Prince Albert behind, and the Queen of England herself tripping down his own railway-station on his arm, as small as a fairy in her pale satin gown and her face all smiles inside her white bonnet. 'Beautiful! really *beautiful! most* gratifying!'

JULY 6
Brothers
(*A Russian Proverb Tale*)

ONE hot day a boy in a shabby coat and a boy in a good one happened to be going the same road. The shabby boy had a mongrel running at his heels, and the well-clad one was riding a trim pony. When the rider overtook the walker —'Hilloa, brother! give us a lift!' he cried.

'Who're you calling brother?' shouted the other.

The rough little mongrel yapped at the dapper pony, the pony flicked his tail and cantered on, and that would have been all if five minutes later a cloud hadn't burst overhead. Before he could reach cover in a copse, the rider was drenched to the skin, and the walker who soon joined him was as wet. The two boys with their shivering beasts stood ill-at-ease under the dripping trees till the storm passed and the sun broke out as suddenly as the cloud had burst. With one accord the boys ran out of the copse, stripped off their clothes, hung them in the heat, and soaked themselves in the light, laughing together, while the dog and the horse barked and whinnied, and shook themselves with delight. When all were warm again the boys pulled on their clothes and prepared to take the road.

'Jump up behind, brother,' cried the rider.

'Who're you calling brother?' laughed the walker.

'We are brothers,' said the other, 'our rags have been dried in the same sun'—and the boys went on together with equal hearts.

JULY 7
The Sun that Warms You

*I*S *it not so, brother?*
The sun that warms you
         warms me,
The fate that forms me
         forms you,
The irk that frets you
         frets me,
The rain that wets me
         wets you,
The hour that tries you
         tries me,
But the sun that dries me
         dries you.
    It is so, brother.

JULY 8
JEAN DE LA FONTAINE *born* 1621
John of the Fountain

*J*OHN of the Fountain was born in July.
With a tale on his tongue and a ryhme in his eye.
France was his mother, and Aesop his nurse—
What wonder that John spouted fountains of verse?

JULY 9

Mrs. Ann Hicks and her Apple-Stall

IN July 1851 Parliament was all in a hubbub about Mrs. Ann Hicks and her apple-stall. Apple-stall indeed! Mrs. Hicks had a positive little estate in Hyde Park. Would the Government please to explain how it had come about? It had come about in much the same manner as the House that Jack built.

Mrs. Hicks had begun modestly by asking permission of the authorities to keep an apple-stall in Hyde Park.

Certainly, Mrs. Hicks!

But after all the public wants more than apples; they likes toothsome goodies, buns, and sweets. Is there any objection?

None whatever, Mrs. Hicks!

But lawks! what a load of stuff now to cart to and fro, when just a little wooden lock-up for the wares would be such a convenience.

Why, to be sure, Mrs. Hicks!

Well, folks must drink as well as eat, and if one sells gingerbread, why not gingerbeer?

Why not, Mrs. Hicks?

Dear, dear, them gingerbeer-bottles are taller than one'd think for, they'll never stand in the little wooden lock-up unless the roof is raised.

Then raise it, Mrs. Hicks.

But wood isn't as weather-proof as it might be, that roof could do with mending, so while one's about it why not a few tiles here and a few bricks there?

Quite reasonable, Mrs. Hicks.

Bit by bit, the wood came down and the bricks went up;

the lock-up store became a nice little house with a nice little chimney and a nice little window. But mussy me! how them bothersome boys do pester a body, plastering their noses against the nice little window and peeking into a body's room, when a few hurdles round about would fence 'em off.

Then put up your fence, Mrs. Hicks.

Well now, an't it a pity to have them hurdles so close to the house?——Step by step, the hurdles receded into the Park, and a nice little garden bloomed inside them.

And in the year of the Great Exhibition in Hyde Park, Parliament became aware for the first time that a cunning little apple-woman had installed her demure little dwelling under the very towers of Sir Joseph Paxton's Crystal Palace, which was just about to glitter on the public. Talk of dignity and impudence! The newspapers hummed, the public took sides, Parliament stormed, the Government explained, and Mrs. Hicks protested volubly; but at last the authorities huffed and they puffed and they pulled her house down, though she fought for her rights to the very last apple.

JULY 10

Five Trees

(It is said that in fifty years the oak, beech, elm, ash, and sycamore will
have almost disappeared from the English forests, because hardwood
trees are in less demand than softwood timber.)

How lovely in the English wood,
  And on the English mead,
These five among our trees have stood
  To serve the country's need.
Must they, like yeoman stock of yore,
  Pass from the rustic realm,
The beech, the oak, the sycamore,
  The ash-tree and the elm?

These have been rafters of our roof,
  Upholders of our walls,
These have made wind and weather-proof
  Our granaries and stalls;
The plough, the waggon, and the yoke,
  The arrow's airy flash,
Came from the sycamore and oak,
  And elm and beech and ash.

On us their spreading arms have shed
  Green shadow like a grace;
Us they have served as board and bed
  And the last resting-place;
Now must they drop their ancient store
  Somewhere beyond our reach,
The oak, the ash, the sycamore,
  The elm-tree and the beech?

JULY 11
A Tree Growing

THERE's an old Forest Charter which runs that if a man
shall build a dwelling upon common land from sunset
to sunrise, and enclose a piece of land whereon there shall be

a tree growing

a beast feeding

a fire kindled

a chimney smoking

and provision in the pot

such dwelling shall be freely held by the builder, 'anything
herein to the contrary nevertheless notwithstanding'. From
sunset to sunrise! There's the rub. Henry David Thoreau,
that man of the woods, might have done it; but I don't
know who else.

JULY 12
HENRY DAVID THOREAU *born*, 1817
The Owls

A MAN of medium height, and sparely built: his eyes now
blue, now grey, deep-set under bold brows; in strong
grey clothes, fit for climbing to a hawk's nest or pushing
through scrub-oak: a man who knew the country 'like a fox
or a bird', and whose feet could find their way through the
trees in the dark: stood one night in the New England
woods, and listened to the hooting of the owls.

'I rejoice that there are owls,' wrote Henry Thoreau. 'Let
them do the idiotic and maniacal hooting for men. It is a

[220]

sound admirably suited to swamps and twilight woods which no day illustrates, suggesting a vast and undeveloped nature which men have not recognized. They represent the stark twilight and unsatisfied thoughts which all have.'

'Wise midnight hags!' cries he. 'They are the spirits, the low spirits and melancholy forebodings, of fallen souls that once in human shape nightly walked the earth and did the deeds of darkness. . . . They give me a new sense of the variety and capacity of that nature which is our common dwelling. *Oh-o-o-o-o that I had never been bor-r-r-r-n!* sighs one on this side of the pond, and circles with the restlessness of despair to some new perch on the grey oaks. Then—*That I had never been bor-r-r-r-n!* echoes another on the farther side with tremulous sincerity, and—*bor-r-r-r-n!* comes faintly from far in the Lincoln woods.'

JULY 13

'Lost upon the 13th inst.'

'LOST, a wire-haired terrier, answers to the name of Paddy':

'Lost, a blue Persian kitten, with orange eyes':

Nobody notices these notices very much, even when a pound or a shilling is offered for the return of the strayed pet.

But if you had lived in 1664, you might have read some such notice as this, which appeared in one of the journals which for the first time were being used for advertisements as well as for news:

'Lost upon the 13th inst., a little blackamoor boy in a blew livery, about 10 years old, his hair not much curled, with a silver collar about his neck, inscribed "Mrs. Manby's Blackamoor, in Warwick Lane".'

Poor little lost blackamoor! Had he run away, in spite of, or because of his silver collar? Had he been stolen by some lady in the next street, who had no little blackamoor, and envied the state in which Mrs. Manby walked abroad? Had he had an accident? Was he ever found, and ever returned, to Warwick Lane, or to the 'Three Cranes' in Pater-Noster Row, where the finder would be 'well rewarded for his peynes'? And when returned, did Mrs. Manby greet him with cries of joy, and give him a saucer of cream?—or did she treat him harsher than her pet spaniel, beat him, and send him supperless to bed?

JULY 14
'Hay-Month'

THE Romans began by calling it Quintilius, the 5th month, because the first month in their calendar was March. After the death of Caesar, Marc Antony renamed the month Julius —July—in honour of his friend.

But the Anglo-Saxons called it Hey-Monath, because this was the month of the hay harvest; and sometimes Maed-Monath, because in July the meadows are at their richest in flowers and grass.

JULY 15

The First Weather Forecast

'St. Swithin's Day, if thou dost rain,
For forty days it will remain:
St. Swithin's Day, if thou be fair,
For forty days 'twill rain nae mair.'

How did the first weather forecast come about?

SWITHIN, Bishop of Winchester, was a good and humble man. He died about two centuries before William the Conqueror, and on his death-bed said: 'Don't bury me with pomp inside the church, bury me in the churchyard where the eaves-droppings will fall on my grave, and the people's feet will tread the grass above me.' So it was done.

But a hundred years later the Clergy of Winchester got together, and one said: 'Brothers, are you aware that that neglected grave in the corner of the churchyard covers the holy bones of Bishop Swithin? It's a crying shame that they don't lie in the Cathedral!' And they appointed a day for the coffin to be dug up and carried, with rites and ceremonies, into the church, where a splendid tomb awaited it.

When the old Saint heard the spades disturbing his sleep, he was very much annoyed. He had enjoyed a century of peace among the lowly things he loved, the swallow nesting in the eaves, the beetle creeping in the grass, and the common folk who came to pray over the humble graves of their kind. He preferred to lie among the peasants of Hampshire, not the Hampshire prelates, and as his coffin was uncovered and hoisted on the shoulders of the monks, he bestirred himself.

[223]

'Rain!' he commanded; and it rained. It rained and it rained. It rained, and it *rained*, and it RAINED. Before the monks could arrive at the church door they were up to their knees in mud; they staggered, they stumbled, and they dropped St. Swithin's coffin on the earth, and went home to change their sandals. If they thought they were coming back next day to finish their short journey, they were very much mistaken. The coffin stuck in the mud, while Swithin's rainfall continued as long as Noah's—just forty days. The monks took the hint, and let the Saint lie where he liked; and since then, if anything upsets him on the 15th of July, he bids the rain to fall, but if he is pleased he bids the sun to shine, for forty days on end.

JULY 16
Swithin's Wish

I'LL lie (*said Swithin*)
Somewhere within
Sound of things
Like birds' wings,
Raindrops' beat,
Insects' feet,
Cows lowing,
Peasants going,
Seeds springing,
People singing,

Boys clattering,
Girls chattering,
Men walking,
Women talking,
Children's tread
(*Swithin said*).
Who shifts the earth wherein I lie
For forty days shall not go dry.

JULY 17

Emily, Bob, and Jane

EMILY, Bob, and Jane
Went for a walk in the rain.

Emily said 'Oh dear, oh dear!
I'll get my best frock wet, I fear,
And my nice new shoes will be covered with dirt,
And my nice clean gloves will take some hurt,
And my hat will lose its fancy shape—
Why didn't I bring my mackintosh cape?'
Emily's one to complain
When she goes for a walk in the rain.

Bob said 'Golly! what fun!
I'll take off my boots and run
In the wettest grass that my feet can find!
I'm soaked before and I'm soaked behind,
But *I* don't care how wet I get,
It's jolly good sport to get thoroughly wet!'—

P

Bob is as happy again
When he goes for a walk in the rain.

And what about Jane?

Jane was thinking 'I wonder
How you'd keep an air-balloon under
The sea, if you happened to get it there?
I wonder if ever a William pear
Could grow on a pearmain apple-tree?
I wonder what people had for tea
Before there was any tea at all?
And why a ball wouldn't *be* a ball
If it was square instead of round?
I wonder what happens to a sound
After I've said it? I wonder why—'

Emily said 'Come into the dry
Under this tree
Out of the rain!'
But Bob only said 'Not me!'
And Jane,
When she heard Emily start complaining,
Wondered 'I wonder *why* it's raining?'

JULY 18

Everyday Word-Meanings: HISTORY

THIS is a Greek word, and it means 'Asking Questions',
or 'Inquiring'. The Father of History was called Herodotus; he lived in Greece, 450 B.C., and was the first man to

write a history book. He thought it would be a good thing for his countrymen to know more about the neighbouring nations, and for years he travelled in foreign parts—in Asia Minor, Syria, Persia, Egypt, and other parts of Africa—seeing things for himself, and asking questions of everybody he met, like a modern reporter. When he had filled his note-books in one country, he went on to learn all he could in the next, and returned to Greece with nine books of what he called his 'inquiries' or 'histories', which he read aloud to those who were curious to hear them.

Three hundred years later, when the Romans conquered the Greeks, the two languages began to mingle as usual, and the Greek word for History became the Latin word 'Historia'. Still later, when the Romans conquered France, they carried the word 'Historia' into the French language, where, very little changed by time, it is still the French word 'Histoire'. Lastly, when William the Conqueror came out of France into England, and French words as well as Frenchmen settled there, 'Histoire' became our own word 'History'. After about five hundred years, people forgot how the word had begun, and began to fancy that it meant 'His-story'. So they chopped off the 'His' and left the 'Story'. A story may still mean history; or it may mean a 'novel', a made-up tale; or it may even mean 'a lie'.

But the chief thing to remember about this word is that it means 'Asking Questions', or 'Wanting to Know', or plain 'Curiosity'—which is the only way for you and Herodotus to find out anything about anything: whether it is about the world, or a word.

JULY 19
Emma's 'Gingerbread' Watch

MISS EMMA ISOLA, a charming young lady, was to be married one July Tuesday, in 1833, to Mr. Edward Moxon. A few days before the wedding (to occur at half-past twelve at St. George's in Hanover Square) her lover sent her a present of her first watch.—'For God's sake, give Emma no more watches,' cried Charles Lamb, in whose house she was staying. '*One* has turn'd her head. She is arrogant and insulting. She said something very unpleasant to our old Clock in the passage, as if he did not keep time, and yet he had made her no appointment. She takes it out every instant to look at the moment-hand. She lugs us out into the fields, because there the bird-boys ask you "Pray, Sir, can you tell us what's a Clock," and she answers them punctually. She loses all her time looking "what the time is". I overheard her whispering, "Just so many hours, minutes, etc. to Tuesday— I think St. George's goes too slow"— This little present of Time, why, 'tis Eternity to her——

'What can make her so fond of a gingerbread watch?'

JULY 20
Old Blue Saucepan

WHEN I shet my eyes now
What do I see?
Blue enamel saucepan
In a green cherry-tree,
Swinging, swinging,

[228]

When de wind is on de day,
To keep dem starlings
            Away.

Won't cook pertaties
Never no more,
Enamel's gone rusty,
Dere's a hole in de floor,
But swinging, swinging,
When de breeze begins to play,
Dat saucepan's bluer 'n
            De day.

Starlings on de flutter,
Breezes on de blow,
An' a blue 'namel saucepan
Where my whitehearts grow,
Swinging, swinging,
To fright de thievin' fray
An' save me my cherries.
            It may.

JULY 21

The Age of a Field-Mouse

WHAT *is the age of a field-mouse?*
    There was once a queer riddle-maker called Wynkyn de Worde, who in 1511 printed his collection of riddles, and called it *Demands Joyous.* His riddles were rather long-winded, and quite impossible to guess by the simple-minded. But who has ever guessed a riddle at a first hearing? The

riddle-asker only waits to hear you say 'Give it up,' so that he may catch you with the smart answer. And when old Wynkyn de Worde wagged his head and demanded joyously: 'What is the age of a field-mouse?' I'll bet a tester nobody got the answer right who didn't know it already. For this is it.

'A year. And the age of a hedgehog is three times that of a mouse, and the life of a dog is three times that of a hedgehog, and the life of a horse is three times that of a dog, and the life of a man is three times that of a horse, and the life of a goose is three times that of a man, and the life of a swan is three times that of a goose, and the life of a swallow three times that of a swan, and the life of an eagle three times that of a swallow, and the life of a serpent three times that of an eagle, and the life of a raven is three times that of a serpent, and the life of a hart is three times that of a raven, and the oak groweth five hundred years, and fadeth five hundred years.'

On hearing which, Hob and Hal and Greasy Joan no doubt slapped their knees and guffawed, 'That's a good un!' And for some odd reason, so say I. But if you joyously demand of me why that riddle seems to me a good one, I shall give it up.

JULY 22

Rats!

ON 22 July 1376 the Pied Piper appeared in Hamelin Town in Brunswick, and piped the plague of rats, and the blessing of children, out of the town for ever. The story is so well known that I won't retell it; if you don't know it, find it in Robert Browning; meanwhile let me tell you something I learned about rats from a lady I met at a party.

The conversation happened to turn on rats and mice. I mentioned that I lived in a yard which once had chickens and horses in it; that brought the rats around, and often, when I sat up late to write, they ran silently over the floor by my chair. They didn't disturb me, and I didn't disturb them, 'but,' I added, 'I never really loved them as I do mice.'

'Mice!' cried the Lady. 'The idea! You can't compare nasty little things like mice with noble creatures like rats!'

'Are rats noble?' I asked, for I am always willing to learn.

The Lady, who was a doctor and a scientist, said, 'I have bred them by hundreds and thousands, and I *know*. I understand and love them. Do you know that mother-rats are as unselfish to each other as hard-working women? When I had two big families, of the same age, one mother would take charge of the other mother's brood, while Mrs. Rat Number One went off for the day to enjoy herself; the next day, Mrs. Rat Number One did the same thing for Mrs. Rat Number Two. Rats have a sense of humour, as well as a sense of humanity. Whenever I had a group of little-boy rats, there was always one among them who played the clown to amuse them, while the rest sat round and laughed.'

'Laughed?' I said (for I am always willing to learn).

'In their own way,' said the Lady, 'they laughed, and showed their amusement. Rats are *darlings*. Don't talk to me of mice!'

JULY 23

Leo

(A Zodiac Song)

T HE Lion with his flaming mane
Burns his way through heaven again.
His voice is thunder in the sky,
And there is lightning in his eye.

JULY 24

ALEXANDRE DUMAS *born, 1803*

When Dumas Gave a Party

W HATEVER Dumas the Elder did, had to be done in the
superlative case. When he decided to give a party, it
must be such a party as Paris had never seen before. So to
begin with he invited all Paris, from the dukes and duchesses
to the clerks and grisettes. And yet, he hadn't five pounds to
give his party with, or a house to give it in. No matter! he
went to his landlord and said, 'My friend! how would you
like to meet the Duc d'Orleans?'

'The Duc d'Orleans! that *would* be an honour!'

'Well, look here, old boy—you know that big empty
mansion of yours in Neuilly—lend it to me for my party,
I'll invite you and the Duke, and there you are!'

'Dear M. Dumas! I shall be delighted.'

So there was the house.

The decorations?—He went round to a dozen of the most
famous artists in Paris, clapped them on the backs, told them

[232]

to come along with him, and locked them up in the empty house until each had painted a whole wall with a masterpiece—for one night only!

The furniture?—He made a tour of his wealthy friends, and got this one to promise his piano, that one his set of gold chairs, another his priceless settees—until the house was furnished from ballroom to buffet.

The food? the drink?—Hum, hum! Dumas was in debt to all his tradesmen—no more credit from them! But he knew the keeper of the king's forests, to whom he said, 'Come to my party, dear chap! and first, lend me the shooting round Villiers-Cotteret for three days. I must give a hunting-party before I give my party.' To his hunting-party he invited all the best shots he knew, and a few bad shots who were good company. They shot hares and pheasants and a dozen fat roebucks. Two bucks Dumas kept for his buffet; the others he dumped on his caterers in exchange for several whole salmon, a gigantic game pasty, loads of confectionery and fruit, and gallons of wine. Then at last he was ready to give his party.

And all Paris came, great and small, some in fancy dress and others not. They dressed as they pleased, and did as they pleased: danced, sang, and caroused till 7 o'clock in the morning, and then, singing and shouting, burst out of the house, and danced in single file back to Paris. The first of them reached the heart of Paris as the last left Neuilly. The procession was three miles long.

That's how Alexandre Dumas gave a party.

JULY 25

'Remember the Grotto!'

A PENNY, kind lady!
Remember the Grotto!
A penny, kind Gentleman,
All for our motto.
   We build our wee cloister
   With shells of the oyster,
   And somewhere inside
   A candle we hide;
   The little wick flames
   In the name of St. James.
But don't ask us why,
For we could not reply,
We ask for a penny
One day in July,
Or what is our motto,
Or why it's a Grotto.

JULY 26

Flower-Names in Dorsetshire

*D*OVES *in the ark* they call Monkshood in Dorsetshire, or sometimes *Lady Dove and her coach and pair*; the Purple Fumitory *Birds on the bough*; the Crown Imperial is *Round-about Gentlemen*; Fritillaries are *Mournful bells of Sodom*, *Codlins and Cream* the Rosebay Willow-herb, and the Wild Clematis is *Devil's guts*. Meadow Saffron they call *Naked maiden*, their Pansy is *Kiss-me-John-at-the-garden-gate*, Red Valerian is *Pretty Betsy*, and Convolvulus *Shimmy and shirts*. They call the Apple *Scrump*, the Potato *Tiddy*, and the House-leek *Welcome-home-husband-though-never-so-late*.

JULY 27

The Seven Sleepers of Ephesus

*I*MAGINE yourself in the City of Ephesus nearly 1,700 years ago.

It is A.D. 250. Christianity is being practised, chiefly in secret; the Emperor Decius is determined to put it down.

Six young Christians, Malchus, Serapion, Maximian, Martinian, Dionysius, and Constantine, are chatting together, when their friend John comes running out of the market-place with Kratim, his dog, at his heels.

Serapion cries, 'What's the matter, John? You look as white as a ghost!'

[235]

'So will you', says John, 'when you see what the Emperor has done.'

'Out with it!' cry the others, and John tells them:

'He has set up an idol in the market-place, and commanded everybody to bow down to it. If we do, we'll be false to our faith; if we don't, he'll find out we are Christians.'

'And if he finds out?' asks Malchus.

John snaps his fingers—'*That* for our lives!' says he.

'I must confess', remarks Martinian, 'I don't much feel like being martyred to-day, and as I have discovered a pleasant cavern on Mount Coelius, let us retire to it until the storm blows over.'

So the seven young men of Ephesus, with Kratim the dog, fled to Mount Coelius, concealed themselves in the cavern, and went to sleep. Kratim also slept.

Two hundred and twenty-nine years later, a labourer from Ephesus halted at a spot on the mountain, thought, 'Here's a good place for my stable,' and began to dig.

'Which of you is snoring so loud?' muttered John, stretching and yawning. 'Shut up there! I can't sleep for your row!'

The other six sat up and rubbed their eyes, and each declared that *he* had not been snoring. Then Constantine asked, 'How long shall we stay here? I'm simply ravenous! let's toss up and see who shall risk death by going down to Ephesus to buy bread.'

The others agreed. The lot fell to John, and with Kratim, the dog, at his heels, the young fellow stole down to one of the city bakeries. But the baker didn't like the look of his money.

'What's the game?' he demanded. 'This old piece is of no use to me.'

'*Old* piece!' exclaimed John. 'Why, it's a brand-new coin, only minted this year.'

'It has the head of the Emperor Decius on it,' scoffed the baker, 'and this same Decius has been dead and gone two hundred years and more.'

'Impossible!' said John.

'Nothing', observed Kratim the dog, in excellent Greek, 'is impossible. There are more things in heaven and earth, John, than are dreamt of in your philosophy.'

John rubbed his eyes, stared at his dog, and said, 'Did you speak?'

'I did,' said Kratim, 'and I do. After one has slept for two centuries, one is either a philosopher or a fool. I don't know what you are, but I am not the fool.'

The miracle of the talking dog persuaded everybody to believe in the miracle of the Seven Sleepers—themselves included; and as soon as it became known, the Christians instituted their Festival upon the 27th of July.

Their names aren't easy to remember; but the Seven Sleepers covers them all quite comfortably. Kratim is another matter; his name is easy to remember, and worth remembering for when he died he became one of the Ten Animals allowed to go to Paradise. The other nine ran to greet him when he came in.

'Sit by *me*, Kratim!' cried Abraham's Calf, Isaac's Ram,

Jonah's Whale, Solomon's Ant, Moses' Ox, Saleh's Camel, Balkis's Cuckoo, and Mohammed's Mare.

'Thanks,' said the Philosopher, 'but I think I will sit by the wisest of you all.'

And Kratim took his place in Paradise by Balaam's Ass.

JULY 28

July's Song

WASH the sheep, and shear the sheep,
 And make my pillow of wool,
Whiles I settle down to sleep
 Beside the washing-pool.
Shear and wash and shear the sheep,
 And drop the fleece again,
Whiles 'tween grass and leaf I sleep
 A-nigh the shearing-pen.
Shear and wash, and wash and shear,
 Soft fall the fleece on me,
The heavy dreaming of the year
 In fertility.

JULY 29

The Old Hermit of Newton Burgoland

'QUAH-QUAH!' said the Old Grey Goose to her goslings, 'men are eccentric creatures, never content with being what they are and wearing the livery they were born in, and few were more so than the Old Hermit of Newton Burgoland who in the year eighteen-hundred-and-sixty-three called himself hermit while he ate and smoked and drank among his fellows, swearing that your true hermit was he who was a solitary in thought, which he exemplified in owning twenty different hats of his own invention, naming them *Patent Tea-Pot*, *Beehive*, and *Odd Fellows*, and embellishing each with a moral emblem, his favourite being one he called *Military*, half cocked-hat, half field-marshal's, with two furred peaks like ears upon the crown, a temptation indeed to the rude boys of Newton Burgoland, who one day made a football of it till it was no longer wearable, whereon the Hermit bewailed its loss to any visitor, declaring it *a perfect beauty, a wonderful hat, costing me many a sleepless night to invent, and many a hungry day to pay for it, never shall I have its like again, for I am old and the times are hard, and cruel audacious boys have nothing better to do than rob the poor old hermit of his noble hat*, which believe it or not, my goslings,' said the Old Grey Goose, 'meant to this old religious maniac what his halo means to a saint, quah-quah!' (*In proof of which, his name was William Lole.*)

JULY 30

'Penn-Sylvania'

WILLIAM PENN, the most famous of Quakers, an Englishman, had a monetary claim upon the Crown; but Charles the Second preferred to keep his guineas, and gave his subject instead a grant of territory in the New World. Penn saw a chance to realize one of his dreams; he would sail with a band of Friends for the Delaware, and found there a colony of Quakers where they might 'practise their convictions in unmolested peace'. And because the land was so rich in verdant forests, he would call this ideal colony Sylvania.

'Nay,' laughed the Merry Monarch, 'you shall prefix it with your name, I insist on it. It shall be Pennsylvania or nothing.'

JULY 31

On this Day the Wren and the Robin stop Singing

CHAFFINCH sings at dawn,
Chiff-chaff sings all day,
Wren and Robin pick the lawn
Without roundelay.
    Sing again, Robin!
    Sing again, Wren!
Ne'er a note and ne'er a note
Till August's out again!

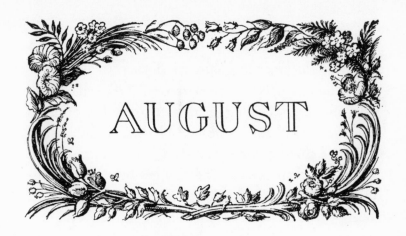

AUGUST

AUGUST 1

The Battle of the Nile, 1798

Casabianca

SEA, be kind to a young Boy's Bones
Who died in Battle in Afric Zones:
When Nelson fir'd his Father's Ship
They took Together her last Trip.

While Others fled the Fiery Breath,
As their Captain lay in Death,
It was this Infant's Only Boast
That he would not quit his Post.

Ere Manhood Learn'd on him to smile,
Dyed in the Battle of the Nile
Casabianca *aetat* 10.
Honour him as you would Men.

AUGUST 2

Purkiss the Charcoal-Burner

ON the 2nd of August, in the year 1100, Purkiss the Char-coal-Burner was riding in his cart towards the hut in the New Forest that was his home. He and his fathers had always burned charcoal there, had always had a horse, a cart, and enough for their needs. The changes brought to England by the Norman had made little difference to him; though to be sure there was more hunting in the Royal Preserves, more cries of '*Tirez! tirez donc!*' in the strange new tongue, and stricter game laws than men had known under the Saxon. There had been hunting that day in the Forest, Purkiss knew; and driving through a deep secluded dell the charcoal-burner came upon one of its victims. At first from afar he took the fallen body for a deer; but drawing nigh he saw it was a man, shot mortally through the breast. The red blood oozing from the wound matched the red of the dead man's hair.

''Tis one of the King's train,' said Purkiss to himself, judging by the rich apparel; and he lugged the body into his wooden cart, and turned his horse towards Winchester, where the King lodged. But when he came to the palace the outcry told him that it was William Rufus himself whose blood stained the wagon-boards; and Purkiss was beset with questions about Sir Walter Tyrrell, who had gone hunting with the King, and not returned. Purkiss could answer no questions; he had not set eyes on the knight, who after that day's accident—if it was one—had made for France, and joined the next Crusade.

Purkiss was let go, and returned to his charcoal-burning; and soon, because he had found and done his best for the King, he was granted a few rods of land in the Forest for his own and his heirs in perpetuity. It made no more difference to him and his heirs than had the coming of the Norman; for hard on eight hundred years the family of Purkiss kept its name, its calling, its hut, its horse, and its cart in the New Forest, living on its own land from father to son, never any richer and never any poorer. Till 1700 at least the axle of the cart that had drawn the King to Winchester hung in the Purkiss's hut; one day it fell down and hurt its owner's foot, and he, in a temper, made charcoal of it. But time has not burnt out its tradition; the name of Purkiss grows sturdy as a New Forest oak; and though there are greater names planted in Hampshire, there is none so ancient.

AUGUST 3
Cherry-Pie Sunday
(An old Buckinghamshire Custom)

CHERRY Pie and Beer!
Come and get 'em now
On Cherry-Pie Sunday
At the Old Plough.
Cherry Pie for you,
Mug o' Beer for me,
Who won't drink Beer
He may drink Tea,

Who won't drink Tea
He may go dry!
Come along to Cadesdean
For Beer and Cherry Pie.

AUGUST 4

PERCY BYSSHE SHELLEY *born, 1792*

'Gifts to Eternity'

*S*HRINE *of the dawning speech and thought*
Of Shelley sacred be
To all who bow where Time has brought
Gifts to Eternity.

This is the inscription over the fire-place in the little room in Field Place in Sussex where Shelley the poet was born.

He was the eldest of six; he had four little sisters and a baby brother. When he was a schoolboy home for the holidays, he would take them on his knee and tell them fantastic tales. When he tramped over the fields with them, he dropped them like puppies over the high fences, climbed over after them, and on they went again. When he romped with them in the garden, he tumbled his tiny brother in the strawberry bed, and the baby told him he was 'a bad Bit!'

Field Place was not far from St. Leonard's Forest, and legend said that a Dragon and a Headless Man lived inside it; while Warnham Pond, hard by, was the home of an Old Tortoise. Shelley used all these fabulous creatures in his games with the children, and peopled their world also with the figure of a Grey Alchemist who was supposed to live in their own garret, and an Old Snake who had been seen in their garden. He was a strange, wild, gentle boy; his fancy had to be at play upon something. One day he dressed his sisters up as little devils, and ran in front of them, carrying a vessel 'flaming with magical liquids'. At another time, wanting 'a little Hell of his own', he set fire to a faggot in the grounds. He saw a small Gipsy acrobat at the door, and told his parents that he wished to adopt the child; he rode his pony through the Sussex lanes, giving away his pocket-money, and when he had no more, he borrowed from a servant to give to a beggar.

The slender boy, with bright hair and blue eyes, was considered a madcap; and when he took to wandering by night, a man was set to watch what he did. 'He only took a walk and came back again', was the report. Only? I would wager that Percy Bysshe Shelley did much more than that—in imagination—on those dark nights when he roamed abroad by himself.

His life was miserable when he went to school. The old boys gathered round to bait the new boy, and when they found that he knew nothing of peg-top, leap-frog, fives, or cricket, could not run a race, and would not fight, they poured derision on him. Yet the boy they mocked till he turned his back and wept, brought 'Gifts to Eternity'.

AUGUST 5

The Child in the Train

THE train stands still
    And the world runs by
Yonder runs a tree
    And a cloud in the sky.
Here flies a pony
    On the running road,
And there flows the quickest
    River ever flowed.

The mountains on the edge
    Roll away like the tide,
The backs of the houses
    Pass on a slide,
The little farms slip off
    As soon as one looks,
And the little churches vanish
    With their spires and their rooks.

The buttercup embankments,
    The telegraph wires,
The names of the stations,
    The small heath fires,
The hoardings in the fields,
    And the people in the street,
Go whizzing into somewhere
    While I keep my seat.

The little cities trot,
   And the little hamlets trip,
The meadow with its cow,
   The sea with its ship,
The forest and the factory,
   The hedge and the hill—
The world goes running by
   While the train stands still!

AUGUST 6
Tide Coming In

IN August 1885 one of Lewis Carroll's young friends went to the sea-side, and felt lonely; she wrote to tell him so, saying she was not what she 'could honestly call happy'. Lewis Carroll wrote back to her from Eastbourne, where he too had gone for a sea-side holiday, and confessed that his first day or two at the sea were always a little depressing—in fact, 'my own experience is, that *every* new form of life we try is, just at first, irksome rather than pleasant'. And then he offers Miss Isabel a bit of philosophy. He tells her not to think about loneliness, or happiness, or unhappiness, for a week or two. 'Then "take stock" again, and compare your feelings with what they were two weeks previously. If they have changed, even a little, for the better you are on the right track; if not, we may begin to suspect the life does not suit you.' It's no use, he says, comparing one's feelings between one day and the next; Isabel must allow 'a reasonable interval, for the *direction* of change to show itself'.

Then he tells her to sit on the beach and watch the waves

for a few seconds. 'You say, the tide is coming in.' But after six waves—'The last is the lowest; it is going out.' But after a quarter of an hour, when it is possible to compare the average place of the sea with what it was when she began to watch, she may be able to say, 'No, it is coming in, after all'.

AUGUST 7
Calypso's Cave

OF all the sea-farers that ever lived in a cave, the greatest and most famous was Odysseus. In his ten years' journey over the wine-dark ocean, driven hither and thither by the gods, he came to rest for awhile on the island of Calypso, the nymph with braided hair, and lived and slept in her cave. The cave, says Homer, looked out on a violet sea, and the great fire burning within filled the isle with the scent of cedar and sandal-wood. It stood in a grove of poplars and sweet cypress, where owls and falcons roosted, and noisy sea-birds; and the walls and roof of the cave were hung with a vine, heavy with grapes. Four fountains of bright water sprang close by, and the tender meadows were blue with violets and white with wild parsley. The fair Calypso sang at her weaving, throwing a golden shuttle. But Odysseus sat upon the shore and wept for his home in stony Ithaca.

AUGUST 8
A Queer Harvest

'QUAH-QUAH!' said the Old Grey Goose to her goslings, 'the queerest Harvest ever reaped was the Rev.

Tide Coming In

Philip Gough.

George Harvest, who died on the Eighth Day of August, Seventeen-Hundred-and-Eighty-nine, and was so absent-minded that he twice forgot his wedding-day to two different brides, so remained a bachelor all his life, and would walk into his own church with a gun under his arm, forgetting it was Sunday, and never had more than sixpence in his pocket to buy what he liked most, which was shrimps and gingerbread, and when lost in the town of Calais where he was to lodge at the Silver Lion, being unable to inquire the way in French, put a silver shilling in his mouth, and did his best to imitate a lion rampant, whereon the natives conducted him, not to his hotel, but to the police station, yet believe it or not, my goslings,' said the Old Grey Goose, 'this eccentric was so valued by the Speaker of the House of Commons that to the end of his days he was welcome to bed and board in Ember Court, where he finally forgot this world for the next, quah-quah!' (*Which is as true as the Gospels the Reverend George forgot to preach.*)

AUGUST 9

Neptune

As Pluto ruled the underworld
In shadowed majesty,
And Jupiter the overworld,
Neptune ruled the sea.

His cavalcade across the waves
Was marvellous to view;

[250]

His Tritons through the windy caves
Of conches music blew;

Great sea-horses his chariot swept
From oceans chill and grey
To purple seas where dolphins leapt
In showers of rainbow spray;

From pearly shells his Nereids peered,
Old Neptune's laughing girls;
His four winds blew his sea-green beard
Into a million curls;

His breakers, tall as emerald towers
With turrets white as milk,
Sank smooth as meadows strewn with flowers,
And left a sea like silk.

Where sun a golden road did blaze,
And moon a silver made:
Thus upon the ocean-ways
Rolled Neptune's cavalcade.

AUGUST 10
Greenwich Time

IT was said of Charles the Second, in his lifetime: 'He never
said a foolish thing, and never did a wise one.' But when,
on the 10th of August 1675, the Merry Monarch laid the
foundation-stone of Greenwich Observatory, he was doing
a wiser thing than he, or the man who made that saying,
knew. He was laying the foundation-stone of time itself.

King Charles could not have foreseen that millions of the great-great-great-great-grandchildren of his subjects would listen-in to Greenwich time every day. It was through the eye, and not through the ear, that Greenwich Observatory gave the exact time daily to numbers of people who needed to know it to a split second. These people were the ships' captains on the Thames. But from their stations in the river they could not possibly have all seen a big clock-face. The Thames near Greenwich is as curly as the letter S, and is crowded with the shipping of the Port of London. Above this forest of masts rises Greenwich Observatory, topped by an enormous ball that can be seen from far and near. At precisely one o'clock (mean solar time) the seamen and merchant captains saw this ball drop down. Ships about to depart on distant voyages depended on this daily signal; captains watched for and set their chronometers by it; and on the correctness of their chronometers hung the calculations of their longitudes.

The exquisite apparatus still works; the ball still falls daily at one o'clock; but the captains who once were lookers-on are now listeners-in.

AUGUST 11

The Two Wheat-ears
(A Belgian Proverb-Tale)

A WIND went through a wheat-field ripe for cutting. Two ears side by side swayed on their stems, but one swayed with a bowed head while the other kept his held high over the rustling field that soon would be sheaves. It was he, therefore, whom the wind noticed first.

'You seem well satisfied with this year's harvest,' said the wind, 'for you hold yourself proudly.'

'Yes, yes,' chattered the upright ear of wheat, 'I've reason to be proud of myself this year. I flatter myself I've earned the country's thanks. I fancy the miller will welcome me with honour. And I think I may say I stand well in the eyes of God.'

'And you,' asked the wind of the ear that bowed his head, 'what are you saying down there?'

The ear answered softly, 'I am saying my grace.'

The wind passed on, observing, 'The empty ear of corn holds its head the highest.'

AUGUST 12
Low and High

IF you are low with humbleness,
  The riches of Christ,
You will give more and say less
  Than the high-priced
Who stalk with empty heart and chin
  Poked up, and give
None of the treasure from within
  By which men live.

AUGUST 13

Everyday Word-Meanings : LADY

HAVE you ever thought of your Mother as the Lady of the House? Have you ever thought of her as the Bread-giver? These are the same thing, and she is both of them. In Ireland to-day, a tramp who comes to the door may still say, 'God bless you, lady of the house,' to the woman who has given him bread. Perhaps she has given him something else—meat, or money, or a cup of tea; but when one thinks of feeding hungry people, it is bread that comes to one's mind. Bread seems to cover what we mean by food. That Irish tramp does not know it, but when he says, 'God bless you, lady,' he is really saying, 'God bless you, loaf-giver.' For the word LADY comes from the Anglo-Saxon, and means 'She who keeps or makes the loaf'.

The Anglo-Saxon word is HLAF-DIGE (the last is two syllables). HLAF was the word for LOAF, and DIGE meant 'The Kneader'; put together they meant 'She who kneads the Loaf'. Perhaps at first HLAF-DIGE does not look to you very much like LADY. But now look again at two important letters in each half of the word: hLAf-DIge. Say aloud those letters, printed in capitals, and there you have your LADY.

As the years go on, the way we say a word changes; a letter gets lost, or is added, the sound of a vowel alters—and so HLAF-DIGE in time turned into LADY, as we say it to-day. Slowly also, the meaning of a word changes, or gets hidden under a new meaning. But to-night, when your Mother cuts the bread for supper, you can say to her: 'Thank you, Lady of the House! Thank you, Keeper of the Loaf!'

[254]

AUGUST 14
The Gleaners

THE field is shaven to its stubble,
   The sheaf is borne away,
Yet here the aged folk bent double
   Go stooping through the day,
To glean with hardly counted trouble
   Some corn to bear away.

Whole families, the old grandmother,
   The woman whom she bore,
The tiny sister, tinier brother,
   All search the golden floor
For one more ear, and then another,
   To swell their scanty store.

The ancient bounty plenty granted,
   How long ago, to Ruth,
Granted to these: but oh, how scanted
   Life's bread must be in truth,
When for a handful sorely wanted
   Age stoops all day with youth.

AUGUST 15
NAPOLEON BONAPARTE *born*, 1769

'An Earthly Paradise'

IN 1502 the Portuguese discovered the island of Saint Helena, where Napoleon was to end his days. A lovely descrip-

[255]

tion is given of the island by Jan Huyghen van Linschoten, who touched there on a voyage in 1592. He speaks of it as an earthly paradise. The Portuguese had filled it with birds and beasts and fruit trees, which flourished with 'an almost incredible abundance'; bucks and wild hogs, hens and partridges, could be taken by hand, or the throwing of stones, so plentiful were they; and the valleys were overrun with figs, pomegranates, oranges, and citrons. Sun, rain, and refreshing streams did their work so well and timely that there was fruit all the year round; and the air was so fine and pure that the island was kept for the landing of the sick, who were left there with rice, biscuit, oil, and spices, and called for, cured, a year later. Every man made his lodging under a tree, Van Linschoten tells us, setting a tent below it—'and the trees are there so thick, that it presently seemeth a little town or an army in the field. Every man provideth for himself, flesh, fish, fruit, and wood; for there is enough for them all: and every man washeth linen.'

The invalids carved their names, or marks, in the trees 'for a perpetual memory: whereof many hundreds are there to be found; which letters, with the growing of the trees, do also grow bigger and bigger'. As far back as 1510 went these names on the fig-trees, 'and every year following orderly'. The oldest fig-trees bore letters of 'the bigness of a span'.

More than a hundred years have slid by since Napoleon died there. Did he, for whom that earthly paradise was a sickness without cure, ever carve his name too in some young bark; and might we discover to-day on an ancient fig the letter N of the bigness of a span?

AUGUST 16
Poppies

COLD reigns the summer, and grey falls the day,
  The flame of the year is smouldering away,
But here in the hedgerow and yonder in the wheat
The flame of the poppy is throwing out its heat.

Small grows the corn and scant is the yield
Of the hay lying strewn upon the stubble field,
But there in the meadow and here by the road
The red poppy glows as in other years it glowed.

Sunrise comes chilly and sunset comes wet,
Low burns the flame where the sun rose and set,
But red as the flame of a dawn that will not pass
The fire of the poppy is lighted in the grass.

AUGUST 17
'Wheat-Month'?

THE Romans called it Sixtilis, the sixth month, and it
  started in their calendar, with twenty-nine days only;
Julius Caesar, in re-making the calendar, managed to give
it another day; and the Emperor Augustus, when he took the
month for his own (as July had been given to Caesar), stole
a day from February, so that he might have as full a month as
any; and February has gone short ever since.

What the Anglo-Saxons called it is a mystery; but because
they called July *Hey-monath*, the month of hay, may they
not have called August *Hweaten-monath*, the month of wheat?
But this is only a guess of my own.

AUGUST 18

Secret Initials

MANY things to-day are shortened by being spoken of by their initials only; but this convenient way of avoiding long descriptions can be a real inconvenience unless you happen to *know* that S.P.C.A. means the Society for Prevention of Cruelty to Animals. A set of such initials is merely a short cut, not meant to hide a secret; but other sets of initials have often been used to hide secrets, great or small. Historical secrets and sentiments, which might have led to the block, were once concealed in a whole alphabet of secret initials, used by the Jacobites in 1746.

It was in this year, on 18 August, that certain important Scots were executed for their part in the rising of 1745. But the Jacobites, loyal to James the Pretender, had ways of toasting and referring to him, by secret codes; and they taught their children an alphabet, which had the following meanings:

A.B.C. A Blessed Change. (*Back to the Stuarts from the Hanoverians.*)

D.E.F. D—— Every Foreigner. (*Meaning King George the Second.*)

G.H.J. Get Home James.

K.L.M. Keep Loyal Ministers.

N.O.P. No Oppressive Parliaments.

Q.R.S. Quickly Return Stuart.

T.U.W. Tuck Up Whelps. (*By Whelps, meaning the Guelphs.*)

X.Y.Z. 'Xert Your Zeal.

A childish game, that couldn't have done the Hanoverians

much harm. But any young Jacobite who could say his alphabet through correctly after dinner to an old one was pretty sure to go off with something extra nice out of the dish of dessert.

AUGUST 19

Tiberius and the Glass

ON 19 August, when the Emperor Augustus died, Tiberius ascended the luxurious throne of Rome. One day a glass-maker begged an audience of him; the Emperor admitted him, and asked what he had to say.

'Nothing to say,' said the craftsman, 'something to show.' And he held up to the Emperor's admiring gaze a superb goblet of glass.

'You wish to sell it, I suppose,' said Tiberius. 'Name your price, for it is a beautiful thing.'

'Noble Tiberius, the glass is yours as a gift. But it is not for its beauty that I bring it to you. O Emperor, this glass contains a secret.' So saying, the glass-maker lifted the goblet high in air, and threw it on the mosaic at the foot of the throne. Those standing by gasped with dismay, and Tiberius with anger; then, to the amazement of all, the man picked up his shining glass, unbroken, and handed it to Tiberius with a smile. 'That is the secret,' he said. 'I have discovered a way to make unbreakable glass.'

But the Emperor's face grew blacker than before. 'Does any other know your secret?' he asked.

'Not yet,' the craftsman reassured him.

[259]

'Good!' The Emperor gave a command: 'Take this fellow
hence and execute him.'

'O Emperor!' cried the man. 'I have done nothing!'

'You have done,' said Tiberius, 'what will make silver and
gold less precious than dirt and dust.'

The man was led away; and for another two thousand
years the secret of unbreakable glass lay hidden.

AUGUST 20

ROBERT HERRICK *born*, 1591

Sweet Robin Herrick

THIS day Robin Herrick
Was born in Cheapside,
His father he laughed
And his mother she cried,
So to sweet Robin Herrick
'Twas given to spy
The tear in the marigold's
Laughing eye.

AUGUST 21

'London Lickpenny'

THERE was a Suffolk countryman called John Lydgate,
because Lydgate was where he was born in 1370, and
he came to London, which he did not like. So he wrote his
London Lickpenny, to tell what he saw there, but he makes
the fellow in his poem a Kentishman, as a thin disguise. Like

countrymen to-day, he chose summer as a good time to come to town to see the sights. Of course he visits Westminster and the Law Courts, where, says he, he might die before anybody, rich or poor, would do a thing for him. At Westminster Gate cooks proffered him 'bread and ale and wine and ribs of beef both fat and full fine', and went so far as to spread a fair cloth for him; but finding he must pay, and having no money, he turned away. In London town he was beset with tempting cries of '*Strawberry ripe!*' and '*Cherries in the rise!*' which meant the green branch of a cherry-tree, leaves, fruit, and all; saffron, and spice, and '*Hot peascodés*' were all cried in his ear; in Cannon Street they offered him hot sheep's feet and mackerel, in East Cheap 'many a pie', and in Cornhill a taverner plucked him by the sleeve and asked him to 'assay' his wine. In Cheapside he is offered silks, lawns, and velvet, and the finest Paris thread; by London Stone the drapers show him cloth; '*Pewter pots!*', '*Rushes green!*' cry others. In Westminster his hood is filched, and in Cornhill he is offered it for sale, where it hangs among much stolen property. At last, foot-weary, he prays a Billingsgate bargeman to carry him in his boat; but as he cannot pay, the bargeman refuses, in good 'Billingsgate' no doubt. And the countryman goes back to Kent, disgusted with London and the Londoners.

AUGUST 22
The Queen's Cable

AT the end of July 1858 the British warship *Agamemnon*
and the American warship *Niagara* met in mid-ocean
and parted; but while one steamed towards England and
the other towards the United States, they were bound together by the first great cable, which they had sunk in the
sea, and were now paying out, mile after mile, East and West.
Nobody believed that the miracle of the submerged cable
could come about; in the bed of the sea writhed this incredible
sea-serpent, thousands of miles long, who was to carry mes-
sages in a few hours from the tip of his tail at one end to the
tip of his nose at the other. And in less than a month it had
come true. On August 22 Queen Victoria in London sent
this message to President Buchanan in Washington:

'The Queen desires to congratulate the President upon
the successful completion of this great international work,
in which the Queen has taken the greatest interest. The
Queen is convinced that the President will join with her
in fervently hoping that the electric cable, which now con-
nects Great Britain with the United States, will prove an
additional link between the two nations, whose friendship

is founded upon their common interests and reciprocal esteem. The Queen has much pleasure in thus directly communicating with the President, and in renewing to him her best wishes for the prosperity of the United States.'

Two hours after the Queen had sent her message, the President was reading it. He answered it 'in a suitable strain'.

And on the 3rd of September, says a contemporary account, the submarine cable 'refused to "speak", and has never spoken since'. No, the whole thing was too fantastic!—a miracle that couldn't come true.

AUGUST 23
Loganberry Spooks

Y o u know the four poles in the garden
Where the best of the logans grow?
The birds they're watching of 'em,
For they're ripening fast, you know.
So to-day my mother she rootled
Among her old white rags,
And 's done up the loganberry poles
In muslin-curtain bags.

But oo! they're looking so queersome!
They've gone such funny shapes
With the bundling up of the crooked poles
In muslin tied with tapes.
One it looks like a hobbling witch,
And one swelled out with wind
Looks like my great-great-grandmother
With her two old maids behind.

When the sun's a-shining
I can laugh at any bird
That longs for logans, and 's frightened
Of anything so absurd.
But when the moon's a-shining,
And white looks more than white,
I wouldn't go near those logan-spooks
A-rearing up in the night——
    Never tell me they're nowt but posts!
    I'll steer clear of the logan-ghosts
    When summer moon shines bright.

AUGUST 24
The Watcher by the Way

IN rough places on dusty roads you will find the blue chicory now, whose German name is *Weg-wart*, the Watcher
by the Way. They have a legend for the flower which might
have come out of the Greek tales of women who change
their forms. The chicory was once a beautiful girl who
stood at the roadside waiting for her lover. He never came,
and she watched for him till she died, after which she was
changed into the summer flower whose blue is all its own.
They say that if you wear chicory those you love will see
you as you wish them to see you. But remember this: chicory
must not be touched with the hand, only dug up with a gold-
handled knife, or one with a handle of stag's horn.

AUGUST 25
The Prize for Virtue

A HUNDRED years ago in France, 25 August was the date for the presentation of a Prize for Virtue. This prize, given annually, was established under the will of the Baron de Montyon, who in his lifetime had awarded prizes for science, medicine, and literature. But when he died he left his prizes, no longer for letters and learning, but for five poor persons whose acts of virtue most deserved it.

In 1823 four women and one man were chosen; and it was the man, Joseph Bécard, who took the chief prize. He was now an old clothesman, but before the French Revolution he had served in a noble house, where a certain Madame Chevilliac used to visit. In 1812 he discovered her in Paris, blind, destitute, and helpless. Bécard took her to his poor lodging, gave her his bed (himself sleeping, or rather, watching over her, from a chair), spent his small takings on food for her, and ate only what broken scraps he could beg for himself. Her suffering made her not only helpless but peevish, but for eleven years the old clothesman tended her patiently, and when she died, in May 1823, he paid for a prayer for her soul, and carved himself a wooden cross for her grave. His case became known to the Académie Francaise, who made the awards, and on 25 August he received the Montyon Prize of 1,500 francs, a gold medal, and Honourable Commendation, as the reward of Virtue.

AUGUST 26
Virgo
(*A Zodiac Song*)

O VER the hilltop
And over the town
The Virgin goes walking
With stars in her gown,
Stars on her left hand
And stars on her right,
She wakes with the twilight
And walks in the night.

AUGUST 27
Fairy Gardens

(In August 1926 a Memorial Park to Hans Andersen was being laid
in Copenhagen, with the figures of his fairy-tales among the flowers
and trees.)

H OW many fairy gardens, Hans,
Have you laid out in childhood's heart!
Long since in mine you laid your plans
Which into instant being start
At the first inward look; and there
The Elder-Mother's sitting still,
And, while the Maids-of-Honour stare,
The kissing Swineherd takes his fill,
Karen's red shoes dance through the day
Urged on by supernatural powers,

And with his nuts the small Ib plays,
And little Ida counts her flowers;
There Thumbelina o'er the brim
Of parti-coloured tulips peeps,
And there the little Mermaid swims,
And there the little Matchgirl sleeps;
There children in their myriads call
On Ole Luke-Oie for a tale,
And there, oh loveliest of all,
For ever sings your Nightingale.

Many a child will never see
The Park laid out by Danish men,
Yet of the kingdom still be free
You raised for them, Hans Andersen——
Where, on the magic wind that blows
From Denmark, they shall smell the breath
Even of the World's most Lovely Rose,
And hear the Bird that banished Death.

AUGUST 28

JOHANN WOLFGANG VON GOETHE *born,* 1749

'Pan Sleeps'

WHEN the poet Goethe was an old man of seventy-five,
he invited his young friend Eckermann to visit him in
his garden-house at Weimar. He lived in 'a dream of profound solitude' in the park outside the town; his white-
washed walls were trellised with roses from the ground to
the roof. Numerous linnets and sparrows had their nests in

the roses. There were peacocks, too, lured from the Prince's park by the poet, with the food they liked best. Behind the white house rose a grassy slope, with fruit-trees in it; a path wound up and down on the other side, to a grove of young oak and beech and birch and fir. They grew thick as the walls of a little grotto over a semicircle of space, and on the hottest summer day the sun could not pierce their shade. 'There is no better refuge from summer's heat than this spot,' said Goethe to his friend. 'Forty years ago, I planted all these trees with my own hand; I have had the pleasure all that time of watching them grow, and for a great part of the time enjoying their cool shade. On hot summer days I sit here after dinner; and such stillness reigns over the meadows and the park, that the ancients would say "Pan sleeps".'

AUGUST 29

George Brann, the Kentish Bird-Scarer

IN August 1866 George Brann, a little boy of nine, went into the fields in the Kent Weald to scare birds for the first time. He knew all the words that would frighten the crows and the pigeons; they had come down to him from his fathers and grandfathers. He walked around the edge of twenty acres of corn shouting:

'Away, birds, away!
You eat too much,
You drink too much,
You carry too much away.'

[268]

Or else:

> 'Run, birds, run!
> The master's coming with a gun.
> You must fly and I must run.
> Away, birds, away!'

Or else:

> 'Back, birds, back!
> You're on the wrong track.
> Back to Headcorn.'

That is, if the crows and the pigeons seemed to be coming from Headcorn; if they came from another quarter, little George Brann shouted the name of another village; and as he shouted he rang a ship's bell, or swung a wooden clapper, or blew a penny whistle, or turned a rattle. His songs were tuneless; singing didn't matter, but 'hollering' did; and the louder a small boy could holler, the more the farmers wanted him for a bird-scarer, when the seeds were being sown. By the time he was sixteen, George Brann's voice was so strong that there wasn't a scarer south of the Thames to touch him.

By the time he was eighty-two he was still making himself wooden clappers in Pepperbox Cottage on Fairbourne Heath, still shouting at the pigeons and crows in the corn. Never been to London in his life; but he could mind the time when the Kentish hills resounded with the shouts of hundreds of bird-scarers, echoing each other in the season. And now there was none to mock him. George Brann was the last of them.

AUGUST 30

A Nursery Song for Shepherdswell in Kent

SHEPHERD'S WELL

Liltingly.

Going through the hop-fields
Upon an August day,
I met a thirsty wether
In fleece of yellow-grey.
I followed through the hop-fields
The ringing of her bell,
And found the cherry orchard
Where the Shepherd had his Well.

The Shepherd was as wise
As the Shepherd's Well was deep.
He let his bucket down
And drew water for his sheep.
'Thirsty weather, Shepherd!'
'Ye've hit it on the nail'——
He let his bucket down again,
And drew it full of ale.

[270]

AUGUST 31

JOHN BUNYAN *died*, 1688

Bunyan's Flute

JOHN BUNYAN, who wrote *Pilgrim's Progress* in prison, did not begin life in a religious frame of mind at all. He was born near Bedford and bred to be a tinker, and in his youth did wicked things like dancing, playing tip-cat, ringing church-bells, and reading *Sir Bevis of Southampton*. In the midst of these frivolities, he dreamed one night that 'fiends were flying away with him', and woke, he tells us, conscience-stricken.

[271]

Presently he joined Oliver Cromwell's army, was converted, and became an eloquent preacher. When he married, he and his wife, 'came together' (he said) 'as poor as poor might be, not having so much as a dish or spoon betwixt us both'.

The Puritans went out, and the Stuarts came in; Bunyan and his preaching were frowned upon, and he was thrown into Bedford Gaol.

'Hold your tongue, and you shall have your liberty,' they told him.

'Let me out to-day, and I'll preach again to-morrow,' was his answer.

It was twelve years before he was set free, and by then he had become so famous a prisoner that people rushed to buy his works and to hear him preach. For all the Stuarts, *Pilgrim's Progress* caught on like wildfire.

In prison, where Bunyan had kept himself and his family by fastening metal tags to leather shoe-laces, a pretty and amusing tale is told of him. The keeper heard flute-music coming from his cell, but when he went in John was sitting on his stool, tagging laces, without a sign of a flute anywhere about him. Again and again the fluting was heard, and again and again the keeper was baffled. The flute was one of the legs of Bunyan's wooden stool, which he had whittled with his knife till he could play on it; and the heavy rattling of the key in the lock always gave him time to replace the stool-leg and sit down on his flute before the keeper could catch him.

SEPTEMBER 1

Heltery-Skeltery

RUN, rabbit, run!
Run to your warren!
The harvest is done,
The meadow is barren,
The corn was your shelter
From stone, stick, and gun,
Heltery-skeltery
Run, rabbit, run!

SEPTEMBER 2

The Bee-Boy

GILBERT WHITE, in his *Natural History of Selborne*, tells of a simple boy who, from a child, 'showed a strong propensity to bees'. He thought of and lived for nothing else. In winter he dozed in his father's chimney-corner, as torpid as a dormouse; but in summer he was as alert as a

s   [273]

weasel, seeking humble-bees and honey-bees in the fields and hedgerows. He ran hither and thither, making 'a humming noise with his lips, resembling the buzzing of bees'; bees would come out of their hives at a rap of his finger, and fearless of their stings he would take them in his hands and suck their honey-bags. He would go about with bees in his bosom, between his shirt and skin. Wherever bees were the bee-boy was, slipping into the neighbours' bee-gardens and upsetting the hives to get at the honey, and, when metheglin was being brewed, hanging about the tubs to beg 'a draught of what he called bee-wine'. His strange affinity with bees was all he had; 'except in his favourite pursuit, in which he was wonderfully adroit, he discovered no manner of understanding,' says Gilbert White. 'He was a very *merops apiaster*, or bee-bird.'

SEPTEMBER 3
The Difference

YOUR eye may see
    And your ear may hear
What the eye of a bee
Or a rabbit's ear
Are looking at and listening to
Every day of the year, like you.

But the rabbit's ear
Will never hear more
Than it heard last year
And the year before;

[274]

And the honey-bee's eye see no new thing
As it looks on the garden from spring to spring.

But while you grow,
And as you change,
You will come to know
New meanings strange
In the things you listen to, said or sung,
And the things you're looking at now you're young.

That, my dear,
Is one reason why,
With your little ear,
And your little eye,
You are quite unlike the rabbit and bee,
Who never can change what they hear and see.

SEPTEMBER 4
The Neat Little Man with the Green Parakeet

SOME years ago I was walking in a London street where the shop fronts, the lamp-posts, the beggars, the motor-buses and taxis, were all so familiar that I did not really see them. Then suddenly I saw something I could not help seeing. A very small, very neat little man, wearing a bowler hat and yellow gloves, crossed the road with small even steps, and passed me; he moved like an automaton, looking neither to the right nor the left, and on his shoulder, as though it were a part of himself, sat a little green parakeet, as smooth and neat as he was. It was not attached to him by a chain or string; it did not flutter or turn its beady eyes;

it paid no more attention than he did to the passers-by. For years this strange little picture rose before my eyes, something seen clearly and vividly, yet quite inexplicable. And one day it was as suddenly explained.

In Chiang Yee's charming book, *The Chinese Eye*, I came on these words: 'We love Nature. . . . We love birds particularly; sometimes in China you will see a man carrying a cage, or with a bird perched on his shoulder, taking his pet for an airing, just as you take your dogs for a run. We take them for a slow stroll in the forest, we put them in a cage and hang it in the trees to let them sing with their companions of the forest, and answer them. We sit down and listen to their singing. We cannot pretend to run as fast as dogs, and so we find birds more companionable.'

I knew at once that my neat little man was a Chinaman, and that what looked strange to me was natural to him; he was taking his green parakeet for a stroll on Hampstead Heath or Parliament Hill, to listen to its companions singing in the trees.

SEPTEMBER 5
The Tale of a Weasel

GIRALDUS CAMBRENSIS was a Welshman who lived in the twelfth century and travelled Wales in search of tales and customs. At Penbroch Castle he met a man who told him the strange tale of a weasel, which Gerald of Wales (to give him his simple name) sets down as a fact.

The man had gone into a room in the castle, where it happened that a bowl of milk was standing, intended for the master's little son. In a corner of the room a sheep's fleece was lying, inside which he discovered a brood of new-born weasels. He gathered up the fleece, weasels and all, carried it to another room, and went back to watch for the return of the mother. When she appeared she ran first to the corner where she had hidden her young, and was roused to fury by the loss of the fleece. Then she made angrily for the bowl of milk, and, says Gerald, 'raising herself up she polluted the milk with her deadly poison, thus revenging, as it were, the loss of her young by the destruction of the child'. On this the man brought back the fleece to its own place; the weasel, excited by her maternal feelings, testified to her joy with little cries, and running back to the bowl of milk, upset it— 'thus, in gratitude for the recovery of her own offspring, saving that of her host from danger'.

SEPTEMBER 6

The Stratford Jubilee

IN the autumn of 1769 David Garrick arranged a grand-
scale Jubilee festival, in Stratford-on-Avon, to commemorate the placing of Shakespeare's bones in the parish church,
150 years earlier. The event drew crowds to Stratford from
all over England.

On September 6, at five in the morning, Garrick's musicians
and singers from Drury Lane went through the town per-
forming a serenade. Guns were fired, the great ones as-
sembled, and there was a public breakfast at nine o'clock,
presided over by Garrick; after which the company repaired
to the church to hear the oratorio of *Judith* conducted by
Dr. Arne. A procession then formed to go to a painted
wooden amphitheatre on the banks of the Avon. The procession was led by Garrick. Here dinner was enjoyed; the
place of honour was Garrick's. After dinner came a performance of songs, composed by Garrick. In the evening,
fireworks and illuminations by Mr. Angelo, with a trans-
parency of Shakespeare between Comedy and Tragedy.
Next day, more guns, more serenades, more peals of bells;
and after breakfast, the crowd flocked to the amphitheatre
to hear a *Shakespeare Ode*, by Garrick, recited by Garrick,
while a statue of Shakespeare was presented to the town, by
Garrick. Boswell declared that while Garrick recited the ode
'he seemed in ecstasy, and gave us the idea of a mortal trans-
formed into a demigod, as we read in the pagan mythology'.

Unfortunately things went less well after this; and in
London, Garrick and his festival became a subject for satire.

Samuel Foote's lampoon is a pungent corrective to Bozzy's transports.

'A jubilee, as it hath lately appeared, is a public invitation, circulated and urged by puffing, to go post without horses, to an obscure borough without representatives, governed by a mayor and alderman who are no magistrates, to celebrate a great poet, whose works have made him immortal, by an ode without poetry, music without melody, dinners without victuals, and lodgings without beds; a masquerade where half the people appeared barefaced, a horse-race up to the knees in water, fireworks extinguished as soon as they were lighted, and a gingerbread amphitheatre, which, like a house of cards, tumbled to pieces as soon as it was finished.'

SEPTEMBER 7
September's Song

IN orchards set yer ladders,
Yer baskets on the ground,
Sort windfalls in the shadders
   Of low-spread boughs around.
Then whoam to kitchen, neighbour,
   Drink deep and sleep you sound!
So let the apple-labour
   In apple-juice be drowned.
      Haw! haw! haw!
Come pass the cider round.

[279]

SEPTEMBER 8
'Yankee Good Cider'

JONATHAN HASTINGS, an eighteenth-century Massachusetts farmer, made, sold, and advertised 'Yankee Good Cider'. As far back as 1713 'yankee' was college slang for 'excellent'. Slang is as catching as the measles; and it is imagined that the word spread from Cambridge, Mass., to the other New England States, whose natives, after they had peppered their talk with yankee this and yankee that, became known as Yankees to the rest of America. Long before that, the Lowland Scots talked of a quick-witted girl as a Yankie, and meant nothing but praise by it; but let nobody call an American 'Yankee' outside the six New England States, for in all the other States, 'Dem's fightin' words!'

SEPTEMBER 9
Nansen Comes Home

ON 9 September 1896 the little *Fram*, that had been farther north than any boat yet built, steamed up Christiania Fjord, with Nansen and his comrades aboard. Three years and more had passed since they began the journey that set them for ever with Odysseus, Marco Polo, Columbus, and all the great adventurers on the sea. The *Fram* was led up the fjord by sturdy slow-moving men-of-war and quick little torpedo-boats. Flags, hats, and handkerchiefs were being waved, the air was filled with shouts, cheers, and salutes, Peppervik was crowded with people and steamers;

radiant faces were all turned to the group of heroic Norsemen who stood bare-headed on their heroic boat. The sun
shone on the last chapter of an epic when, with thirteen guns
apiece, the men-of-war saluted; and the old fort of Akerhus
answered with thirteen peals of thunder.

'In the evening, I stood on the strand out by the fjord,' says
Nansen. 'The echoes had died away, and the pine woods
stood silent and dark around. On the headland the last
embers of a bonfire still smouldered and smoked, and the
sea rippling at my feet seemed to whisper: "Now you are
at home." The deep peace of the autumn evening sank
beneficently over the weary spirit. . . . The ice and the long
moonlit polar nights, with all their yearning, seemed like
a far-off dream from another world—a dream that had come
and passed away. But what would life be worth without its
dreams?'

SEPTEMBER 10

WILLIAM THE CONQUEROR *died* 1087

Birds and Princes

THEY say that when William the Conqueror lay on his
death-bed in Rouen, he considered his possessions, and
the future of his three sons, Robert Courthose, William
Rufus, and Henry Beauclerc. When they were boys he had
consulted his councillors about them and the wise men had
answered: 'Their fate will depend upon their characters.'

'What *are* their characters?' asked William.

The councillors withdrew, to put one and the same question to the three young princes. First, Robert Courthose.

[281]

'If God had made you a bird,' they asked, 'what bird would you choose to be?'

'A hawk,' said Robert, 'because it is gallant and courteous, like a knight.'

'And you?' they asked William Rufus.

'An eagle,' said he, 'because it is the king of birds, feared by them all.'

'And you?' they asked Henry Beauclerc.

'A starling,' said he, 'because it lives simply, without robbing or hurting its neighbours.'

The councillors returned to the King, and said: 'Sir, your son Robert will be valiant and honourable, your son William will be powerful and hated, and your son Henry will be prudent and peaceful.'

Remembering their words as he lay dying, the Conqueror left his Dukedom of Normandy to Robert, his Kingdom of England to William, and his riches to Henry—who lived to reign prosperously over both Normandy and England.

That is the tale they tell, and you need not believe it; but that's no reason why you shouldn't hear it.

SEPTEMBER 11
The Favourite Fruit

IF you of all the fruits that be
    Could choose a fruit to bite,
Which tree would be your favourite tree
At morning, noon, and night?

There's oranges for golden drink,
And cherries for bright toys,
And melons where you almost sink
Your face in mushy joys.

There's plums as purple as the dusk
And clear as yellow moons,
And mangoes that out-sweeten musk,
To eat with silver spoons.

There's gooseberries whose furry coats
Like caterpillars grew,
And currants black as music notes
And bright as drops of dew.

No, none, no, none of mine are these!
Like Adam I was born
To go and seek the apple-trees
By noon and night and morn;

The green, the yellow, and the red,
The streaky pippin-stripe,
The windfall, and the still unshed,
The ripe and the unripe—

If I of all the fruits that be
Can choose which fruit I'll bite,
My favourite tree's the apple-tree
By morning, noon, and night.

SEPTEMBER 12
'So sure as you've an orchard'
(An English Proverb Tale)

IT'S all very fine (*said old Jane*) to call him Generous Johnny, but when generosity makes a convenience of you I'd give it another name, so I would. The trees are dropping with fruit, the ground is rotting with 'em, the wasps are over-drunk and over-eaten, and folks is standing by the roadside offering baskets of apples for nothing to the motor-folk who won't even stop for 'em. Yet here must he come dumping a barrowload of his second-best windfalls on me that can't cope with my own. Generous Johnny indeed! Anybody can be generous in a good fruit-year, when apples is nothing but a nuisance. Now if he'd brought me fuel for fire, sugar for sweetening, or jars for jelly and jam, that would be more like it. Or if come a poor fruit-year he brought a pocketful of pippins, I'd call him Johnny Generous, so I would. But so sure as you've an orchard (*grunted old Jane*) somebody'll bring you apples.

SEPTEMBER 13
Apples go begging

DO you want apples?
John said to Jenny.
I have got apples
Ever so many.
Do you want any
Russets and ribstons?

I'll give you apples
And charge ne'er a penny.
Thank you, *said Jenny*,
Pippins and Pearmains,
I have *got* apples
Many too many.

SEPTEMBER 14
Aldiborontiphoskyphorniostikos!

ODDS NIPPERKINS! cried Mother Bunch on her broomstick, here's a to do! as Nicholas Hotch-Potch said, Never were such times, when Muley Hassan, Mufti of Moldavia, put on his Barnacles to see little Tweedle gobble them up, when Kia Khan Kreuse transmogrified them into Pippins, because Snip's wife cried, Illikipilliky! lass a day! 'tis too bad to titter at a body, when Hamet el Mammet, the bottle-nosed Barber of Balsora, laughed ha! ha! ha! on beholding the Elephant spout mud over the 'Prentice, who pricked his trunk with a needle, while Dicky Snip the Tailor read the proclamation of Chrononhotonthologos, offering a thousand sequins for taking Bashaw of three tails, who killed Aldiborontiphoskyphorniostikos.

'And that, my goslings,' said the Old Grey Goose, 'was *not* quacked and invented by me, who, say what they like, speaks nothing but sober truth, but was a farrago from a book called "Aldiborontiphoskyphorniostikos" which was intended for little children a hundred years ago, after which let any fool that thinks I talk nonsense go and ask for it at his bookseller's *if he can*, quah-quah!' (*And that's the truth, if not the sober truth.*)

SEPTEMBER 15
The First Balloon

EVEN to-day, when they are nearly as common as birds, aeroplanes flying overhead make us stand and look up; even to-day we stop whatever we are doing to stare and wonder at men who fly in the air. Imagine yourself a boy or girl in the Artillery Ground at Moorfields, on 15 September 1784, waiting to see the first balloon go up over England —the first, that is, with a man attached to it! He was a young Neapolitan, called Lunardi.

On the grand occasion the great open space of Moorfields was crowded with incredulous spectators. There was some delay in getting started, and after an hour or two the crowd passed from impatience to threats. But when at last the balloon rose into the air, the effect, said Lunardi afterwards, 'was that of a miracle, and the multitude passed from incredulity and menace into the most extravagant expressions of approbation and joy'. Waving his three-cornered hat in one hand, and the Union Jack in the other, Lunardi floated out of sight, coming to earth eventually in North Mimms. Up he went again, and alighted near Ware, so frightening some labourers that nothing would induce them to come near the balloon and help him. A young woman was the first to dare to grasp the rope he had thrown out.

After this, the young aeronaut became the rage. He was presented at Court; wigs and hats were named after him; there were Lunardi dresses and Lunardi ribbons; he turned a pretty penny by exhibiting his balloon at the Pantheon in Oxford Street; and it is said that during an important Cabinet meeting the King observed: 'My lords, we shall have an opportunity of discussing this question at another time, but we may never again see poor Lunardi; so let us adjourn the council and observe the balloon.'

SEPTEMBER 16

Hunger-Harvest

THE hay's long cut,
  The corn is in,
The apple-orchard's
Light and thin.

The ricks are thatched,
The barns in store,
The shelves and garrets
Groan once more.

God help the grass
That did not yield,
God help the stricken
Harvest-field.

God help the trees
Pinched by the rime
That killed the fruit
In blossom-time.

God help the folk
That looked to these,
The corn, the clover,
And the trees.

Where apples fail
And wheat is thin
The hunger-harvests
Now begin.

SEPTEMBER 17
'Barley-Month'

THE Romans called it September, because it was the
seventh month in their calendar; and when they brought
their calendar into our country, we took the names of the
months as we took much else they brought us, and stuck to
them even after the year had moved back a couple of paces,
which made September the ninth month instead of the
seventh.

But the Saxons called it *Gerst-monath*, or barley month, because this was the month in which they cut their favourite crop and made barley-brew, before hops were known or thought of.

SEPTEMBER 18

DOCTOR SAMUEL JOHNSON *born* 1709

A Toast for Doctor Sam

*(In Lichfield, his birthplace, Johnson's day is celebrated with punch
and beefsteak pudding)*

WE'LL fill our cups and drink to you
    In Lichfield, Doctor Sam,
We'll fill again and clink to you
    With many a potent dram;
The fumes of punch by candlelight
    Shall from the bowl escape,
And as we keep your natal night
    Perhaps we'll see your shape,
Your great unwieldy shambling suffering well-belovèd shape,
    And hear you boom some word of might
    Or devastating jape.

We'll pile our plates and eat to you,
    Good Doctor, till we burst,
The pudding that was meat to you
    Shall bolster up our thirst;
Its savours in the candlelight
    Shall be our annual choice,
And as we keep your natal night

Perhaps we'll hear your voice,
Your domineering thundering un-contradicted voice,
And see the smile that took delight
Where jolly bucks rejoice.

SEPTEMBER 19

DR. BARNARDO *died* 1905

Nobody's Children

THEY slept where they could, under tarpaulins, among
the warehouses in the East End of London, hundreds
of boys without parents, or any one to care where or how
they slept. Their clothes were the filthiest rags. Their food?
Only what they could cadge or pinch.

Thomas John Barnardo, barely twenty years old, was a
medical student, and an Evangelist. He held simple services
in an East-End Mission House, to which the small starved
urchins sometimes came. One night little Jim Jarvis lin-
gered on.

'Time to go home, Jim,' said young Barnardo.

'Ain't got none,' answered Jim.

That opened the student's eyes to the awful facts. He was
determined that these hopeless boys should be given a living
chance; he had no money, but he had fire and faith. The rich
and melancholy Earl of Shaftesbury was an Evangelist like
himself. The student sought out the Earl, and took him in
a cab at midnight to one of the worst parts of the city. The
cab could not enter the grim alleys through which the two
men threaded their way into a warehouse where heaps of
goods were covered with tarpaulins. Barnardo knelt, and

feeling beneath one of them dragged out a frightened, ragged boy.

'No,' smiled Barnardo, 'we are not the police. Now show this gentleman where the rest of you are.'

The boy jumped from one tarpaulin to another and danced on it. One by one the covers were turned back, and a little white face peered out.

It was enough to open Lord Shaftesbury's purse. In 1867 the first Barnardo Home was opened in Stepney, and the young student had begun to earn his name of 'The Foster-Father of Nobody's Children'.

SEPTEMBER 20
A Shower of Fish

ON 20 September 1839 an English officer stationed near Calcutta was caught in a sharp shower of rain, in the midst of which fell a shower of little fish, three inches long and all of a kind. They did not come helter-skelter, but in one straight line from the clouds to the ground. The fish were alive and kicking; those that came down on hard ground died at once, but those that fell in the grass continued to kick. It sounds fantastic, but it is true; as true as that Major Mackenzie of Fodderty, three miles from the sea, had his farm rained on by a deluge of herrings, that two gentlemen of Toulouse, caught in a storm, were overwhelmed by a cloud-burst of frogs, and that a valley in Norway was immersed in a downfall of rats.

[291]

SEPTEMBER 21

(On this day the year's quarrels among the farm-labourers are settled as follows at Bere Regis in Dorsetshire)

Behind the Gorse

IF quarrel you must, good men of Bere
 That work in the corn and hay,
You shall save up your quarrels throughout the year
  Until Saint Matthew's Day.

If you cannot agree for good or ill,
  You men of the corn and hay,
You shall come to the gorse on Woodbury Hill
  With your neighbours to see fair play.

You shall not argue it round about,
  You men of the corn and hay,
You shall take off your coats and have it out
  In the good old-fashioned way.

And when you've settled the bygone year,
  You men of the corn and hay,
Go down to Bere for a round of beer
  To wash bygones away.

SEPTEMBER 22
The Pet Oyster

OYSTERS are in.

So let me take the opportunity of telling you about the Gentleman of Christchurch who once kept a pet Oyster. Yes, really. It was a particularly large Oyster, of, says report, a very fine breed; none of your mongrels for this oyster-loving Gentleman of Christchurch. He fed it on oatmeal, at regular hours, when it regularly opened its shell to take in its dinner. Sometimes, for a real treat, the Gentleman took his pet down to the beach, and let it go in bathing, but not too far; just a dip and out again. The giant Oyster was so happy at home that it never tried to escape. And then, it would have missed its mice, I expect. For this remarkable Oyster was 'an excellent mouser'; by the time he came to be reported in the press he had already killed five. Mice, it appears, were attracted by the briny smell when the succulent bivalve opened his shell. 'Better than cheese!' they squeaked, poking in their heads. Alas for them! they did not live to regret it.

But whether the Oyster ate them after beheading them is not told. For my part, I can't see why not. I am prepared to believe anything of the Gentleman's Oyster. I am prepared to believe he could have decapitated a Carpenter and devoured a Walrus. The pity is, they hadn't been born in 1839, when the Christchurch Gentleman's Pet Oyster was in his prime.

SEPTEMBER 23
Libra
(*A Zodiac Song*)

THE gold scales of heaven
See how they swing
With fruits of the fall
That were flowers in the spring.

Fill the gold scales
With apples and pears,
Seraphim, Cherubim,
Come for your shares.

Weigh the gold scales
With damson and plum,
Come, saints and angels
And archangels, come.

SEPTEMBER 24

Harvest Home

THE long tables in the big farm-kitchen are loaded with home-brewed beer, home-pressed cheeses, home-baked bread, home-cured bacon, home-made pies and pasties, and mighty joints of meat. Every worker on the farm sits down to the feast; and before they sit, a big wheelbarrow is found to be outside the kitchen door. It is for them that can't walk home at the end of the feast; and they'll need strong heads, for the farmer's beer isn't milk-and-water, and a toast must go round for every sort of person present, from the Master to the Milkmaid, from the Mistress to the Traveller at the door.

The King's Toast sets it off:

'This is the King's health and it shall go round,
    Heigho! heigho! heigho!
And they that don't like to drink the King's health
    Must take up their hats and go.'

The Master's Toast next, which ends:

'Drink, boys, drink!
And see you do not spill,
If you do you shall drink two,
For it is your Master's will.'

Then comes the Dame's health:

'For him we drank one glass, for her we'll drink two,
And we will be merry before we do goo!'

Then a Toast for the Maids, which is not always sung to

[295]

the end, if the Mistress was strict; for the words are a bit too free to suit all ears. The Woodcutter's Toast is sung with action, the drinkers pretending to bind a faggot as this toast goes down. For the Miller they bang their tankards on the table, as they spell out the letters of his good dog's name: 'B! A! N! G! O!' But the Traveller's Toast is the tricky one. The full tankard is set in a hat; the drinker holds the hat-brim on either side, and must drain the tankard without touching it with a finger:

'I've been to France and I've just come from Dover,
I've been a-travelling all the world over.
        Over! Over! Over and o-o-ver!
Drink up your liquor, and turn the bowl over!'

And mind you don't spill a single drop of the liquor as the hat tilts 'over and o-o-ver', for this toast must be drunk and drunk again, till the drinker succeeds, or comes to the wheel-barrow.

SEPTEMBER 25
This Bread

THIS bread,
    This bread
That carelessly you crumble,
    Was once the red
Wheat, the green oat, the humble
    Barley that filled
The dreams of the unfed,
    Man, woman, and child.
Respect this holy bread.

Harvest Home

SEPTEMBER 26

Mrs. Balwhidder's Brass Jelly-Pan

M RS. BALWHIDDER had a brass jelly-pan. What she preserved in it for her husband, the Reverend Micah Balwhidder, before the summer of 1760 I really can't say, for till that year nobody but the rich made jelly and jam. The poor did not plant fruit, and sugar was a luxury.

Then new roads to the Clyde were opened up North, and carriers from the villages and sailors from the sea travelled freely to and fro; and a stream of sugar was set flowing through Scotland. The young men came off their ships from Jamaica or the West Indies, bringing sugar to the villages in quantities unknown of. The same year, by a sort of providence, the villagers had begun to plant gooseberry and currant bushes in their kail-yards; and so, that summer and autumn, jelly and jam-making set in all over Scotland. Which occasioned, said the Reverend Micah, 'a great fasherie' to Mrs. Balwhidder, for she had the only brass jelly-pan in the village, and there was no end to the borrowing of it. But when Mrs. Toddy of the Cross-Keys bought one for herself, it took turn and turn about with Mrs. Balwhidder's.

From then on jelly and jam became an institution in Scotland, and jelly-pans continued to be borrowed till in a hundred years almost every kitchen had one of its own. It took still longer for the idea of jam for tea to become a fashion, and then a matter of course, in England, and for English housewives to start arguing, as the Scots were doing, whether the jam should remain twenty minutes or half an hour on the fire after it had come to the boil. As for the obstinate woman who insisted on keeping hers bubbling for an hour, by which time it was candy, her indignant old servant cried that she 'boiled the very judgement out o't!'

SEPTEMBER 27
Everyday Word-Meanings: JAM

As you sit indoors chewing a slice of bread, somewhere outside a horse may be champing his oats. Champing and chewing, the horse and you are doing the same thing, you are making jam; he of his oats and you of your bread, whether it has jam on it or not. 'Champ' and 'jam' are actually the same word. Long ago, when 'champ' was spelt without a 'p', cham was the word for chew, and also for any pulp that was produced by 'chamming'.

Four hundred years ago Sir Thomas More, writing about diet for babies, said the 'strong meate must be chammed afore by the nurse, and so putte into the babe's mouth'—in other words, the nurse must herself chew, or make jam of, the food which the toothless baby couldn't 'cham' for itself. Trained nurses to-day would hardly approve of this sort of jam for babies. But people were chamming their food long before the Scotch good-wives thought of making soft fruit into jam by boiling it. When they did, it was natural for them to give the name of jam to the pulp they put into their pots. Had not the fruit been 'chammed' by the fire, as, eaten raw, it would have been 'chammed' by their teeth?

As for that horse, he can 'jam' his oats for himself, but not his bit, however hard he champs it—and perhaps, because he couldn't, the hard letter 'p' clamped itself on to the soft word 'cham'. Perhaps we shall not hear him champ his bit much longer, for the horse in the street is becoming as rare as the mammoth, and soon there may be nothing left but motors to make a 'jam' in the traffic on the roads, and airplanes to make 'cham' of the clouds.

SEPTEMBER 28

Spinners in the Sun

THEY spin for life that is their need,
They spin for life that looks like greed,
They are unconscious as they spin
Of the stuff they labour in,
Save as it serves dear life to feed.

In the autumnal air their nets
They hang, and as September wets
The web with dew, or shines in it
Until the film with light is lit,
The eye that looks on it forgets

The reason why the work began;
The wondering eye of child and man
Sees only that the spinners' pains
Caught beauty in its filmy chains.
The spiders knew not what they span.

SEPTEMBER 29

MICHAELMAS DAY

The Michaelmas Goose

ST. MICHAEL'S DAY is a sorry day for rent-payers and geese. But how came geese and rent-payers to be connected with St. Michael, that most militant Saint in the Calendar? Whenever St. Michael is mentioned in the Scriptures, it is with sword in hand. But of goose and rent-payer, no word at all. How can we link them up?

The Middle Ages were full of superstitions which influenced all sorts of local matters outside the church. People believed that certain powerful saints presided over certain days, and they chose suitable Saints' Days for their elections. St. Michael with his sword being the protector of mankind, they set apart 29 September for electing those other protectors of mankind, the magistrates. The day became a feast-day, which the elected lords and magistrates celebrated with special richness. In the fourteenth and fifteenth centuries the peasants who rented their lands from the lords had often to pay their rents in kind as well as in cash; and while the rose-nobles went into my lord's coffers, the best of what was in season came to his table. So that these succulent 'rents' were most welcome on feast-days.

It is set down, in the reign of Edward IV, that one John de la Hay was bound to pay one William Barnaby, Lord of Lastres in the county of Hereford, One Goose fit for the Lord's Dinner, on the Feast of St. Michael the Archangel. No doubt the Lord of Lastres had a larderful of good stubble geese brought in to him at Michaelmas, and sent them round among his friends as certain lords to-day dispense braces of pheasants. It is pretty certain that no newly elected magistrate sat down to celebrate his Michaelmas dinner without a goose to grace it; and if the magistrate was also a lord, he was helping himself to his own rents, as he carved the bird and ladled out the stuffing. And that is how the goose, the rents, and the sword of justice all come together on St. Michael's Day.

SEPTEMBER 30

Farewell to Summer

FARE you well
in your golden shawl,
loveliest Summertime
of all.

Go your ways
with your deep blue eyes,
your tropic nights,
your Italian skies.

Go your ways
with your glowing skin,
apricot, peach,
and nectarine.

Go your ways
with your gleaming hair,
that burned the wreath
of roses there.

You raised our harvests
before their hour,
scorched the herbage
and forced the flower;

but brought such joys
in your shining train
as we may not know
for years again.

In your glittering nights
and dazzling dawns
you turned our youth
into nymphs and fauns,

enchanting us
with bewildering sweet
rapturous light
and radiant heat.

Dreaming October
turns the page.
Fare you well,
O Golden Age!

Go your ways
in your golden shawl,
loveliest Summertime
of all.

OCTOBER

OCTOBER 1

After-harvest

Now the last apple
Trembles on the bough,
The spider's grey silk
Spreads its jewels now.

Fields have been gleaned,
The stubble stands un-eared,
Spring's joyous traveller
Grows his winter beard.

Woolly mists
On midnight meadows creep,
And earth lies chilled
In after-harvest sleep.

OCTOBER 2

Big Ben

BIG BEN is a youngster among the bells of London; he was born in October 1858, and is not yet a hundred years old. He is still a baby to the Great Bell of Bow, and never played Oranges and Lemons with the Bells of St. Clements. But in his brief lifetime he has gained a personality that is almost as legendary as Gog and Magog, and nearly as national as John Bull. Before he rang upon the public's ears he was christened St. Stephen; but some writer in *The Times* nick-named him Big Ben, the name caught on, and he was never called anything else.

He made a bad start with the Houses of Parliament. A month after that October day when his 25 tons had been raised 200 feet in air, his voice cracked. Politicians complained of him, professors analysed him, Parliament went to law about him; and there was such a public shindy that his bells stopped ringing and his hands went out of action. Two years later Earl Derby held him up to ridicule before the House of Lords.

'We all know the circumstances under which we have been deprived of the doubtful advantage of hearing the tones of the great bell,' said he, 'but when a clock ceases to address itself to the sense of hearing, that is no reason it should decline to present itself to the sense of sight. One of the hands has disappeared altogether, and the other stands at twelve; so that it has the merit of being right at least once in the twelve hours.'

'I rejoice,' said Earl Grey, rising after Earl Derby, 'that the great bell has been cracked, and trust no attempt will be made to make the clock speak to our ears again in the old tones.'

Big Ben still speaks, to Britain, and to the world; no other bell is so loved and listened for; and when he vibrates the wave-lengths with tremulous profundity, it is London calling from Westminster to the ends of the earth.

OCTOBER 3
The Spendthrift

OUT of your treasury, dear year,
You squander your last blue and gold.
Your summer held no days more clear
Although they had no tang of cold.
Sweet is the air with which you've swept
The withered leaf along the road;
You have a richer sunset kept
Than any May or August showed.
Unstintingly you spend your store
And fling bright day upon bright day
Until you are stripped bare once more.
And to the end must beg your way.

OCTOBER 4

Brothers and Sisters

COME forth, O beasts! This is the day
  Of that dear Saint who called you brother,
Who greeted you upon the way
  As one companion does another,
And saw in God's creative plan
No difference between beast and man.

Fly down, O birds! This is the day
  Of that sweet Saint who sister named you,
Who, coming in your midst to pray,
  By love, and by love only, tamed you,
And read in the Creator's word
Equal delight for man and bird.

What! not one furry thing runs out?
  What! not a single flying feather?
Men separate with fear and doubt
  What love was wont to bring together.
To bird and beast we call in vain
Till Brother Francis walks again.

OCTOBER 5

The Watchmaker of Rennes

IN the autumn of 1938, in the town of Rennes in Brittany,
died Emile Floch, a watchmaker. He appears to have been
a sort of latter-day St. Francis; when he walked in the streets

[307]

four or five swallows would fly about him, and follow him home. On his walks, too, a partridge strutted behind him. In eight days he tamed a toad so that it would eat from his hand, and birds would alight on him in the presence of strangers, their fear of others conquered by their confidence in him. On his strolls in the woods he carried a martin in his coat, and let it fly in search of insects; but at his word or whistle it flew back instantly, and hopped into his pocket.

OCTOBER 6
The Tale of a Flat

IN the autumn of 1936, during the great Paris Exhibition, a quarrel broke out between the landlord of a flat and his tenant, and a new point in French Law arose.

Paris was crowded with visitors seeking lodgings, and one day a visitor from a French colony knocked at the landlord's door.

'Good day, Monsieur Landlord!'

'Good day, Monsieur Colonist!'

'Have you a flat to let?'

'But yes! a beautiful flat!'

'Let me see it. Good! How much is it?'

'It is so much a month.'

'Very well, I will take it.'

'Not so fast, Monsieur Colonist. There are always certain rules when one takes a flat.'

'What are these rules, Monsieur Landlord?'

'Have you a dog? If so, I cannot allow you to live in my beautiful flat. The rule is, No Dogs.'

'Don't worry, Monsieur Landlord. I have no dog.'

'But perhaps you have a cat. The rule also is, No Cats.'

'I have no more cats than dogs.'

'Ah, but, Monsieur Colonist, it is possible you have a parrot. The last rule is, No Parrots.'

'I have neither parrot, cat, nor dog.'

'In that case I am delighted to accept you as my tenant.'

When the lease was signed, the landlord said, 'I trust you will enjoy your stay in Paris. You have come, doubtless, for the Great Exhibition.'

'Quite right,' smiled the colonist. 'I am taking part in the Great Exhibition. I go now to my duties there and will return to-night.'

And that night the colonist returned to the flat, and brought with him—a camel.

'What is this?' cried the astonished landlord.

'It is quite plain what it is,' said the colonist.

'A camel?'

'A camel.'

'But I do not allow camels in my flats!'

The colonist looked in the lease. 'No dogs. No cats. No parrots. There is nothing at all about camels, Monsieur Landlord.' And he led the camel into the flat.

There he kept it by night, and took it by day to the Great Exhibition.

In the end they carried their quarrel to the courts. The landlord argued that under the circumstances a camel was a dog. The colonist argued that under any circumstances a camel was a camel. It was left for the Law to decide; and how it decided I've never found out.

OCTOBER 7

October's Song

THE forest's afire!
  The forest's afire!
The maple is burning,
The sycamore's turning,
  The beech is alight!
Make a pyre! make a pyre!
Bring the oak to the fire!
The forest is glowing!
The greenleaf is flowing
In flame out of sight!

OCTOBER 8

The Salamander

THE great Italian craftsman, Benvenuto Cellini, who lived in Florence in the Middle Ages, and made wonderful things in gems and ivory and gold and silver, has left us this recollection of his childhood.

'When I was about five years of age, my father happened to be in a little room in which they had been washing, and where there was a good fire of oak a burning: with a fiddle in his hand he sang and played near the fire, the weather being exceeding cold: he looked at this time into the flames, and saw a little animal resembling a lizard, which could live in the hottest part of that element; instantly perceiving what it was, he called for my sister, and after he had shewn

[310]

us the creature, he gave me a box on the ear; I fell a crying, while he, soothing me with his caresses, spoke these words: My dear child, I don't give you that box for any fault you have committed, but that you may recollect that the little creature which you see in the fire is a Salamander; such a one as never was beheld before, to my knowledge; so saying, he embraced me, and gave me some money.'

OCTOBER 9

Everyday Word-Meanings: MANTELPIECE

IMAGINE an old lady with her head and shoulders mantled in a shawl. Then look at any fireplace, with its shelf above and its framework of wood or marble all round it. We may fancy the fire is the old lady, and the structure around it is the old lady's 'mantle'.

'Mantle' and 'Mantel' are the same word, and why they should be spelt differently it is hard to say. This is one more of the words that came to us from France. The French word for a cloak is *manteau*, but the old French was *mantel*; and in the old fireplaces the mantel sloped forward like a hood, to catch the smoke and keep it out of the room. Later on, when the chimneys were made more cleverly to draw up the smoke, the mantelpiece became less like a hood, and more like a frame round the picture of the fire. But it still supported a shelf which jutted forth like a covering for the old lady's head. And the next time you arrange flowers on the mantelpiece, you may tell yourself that you are trimming the old lady's cap, or putting a rose in some Spanish beauty's mantilla.

OCTOBER 10
Followers of the Sun

AND whither, black-eyed gypsies,
  Oh whither do you go
When summer's past to 'scape the blast
  And shelter from the snow?
So sure as swallows vanish
  The way the sunbeams run,
So sure the crew of gypsies too
  Goes following the sun.

Oh is it back to Egypt
  Or back to Hindustan,
To some dim age in history's page
  They drive their caravan?
Where do they spell their fortunes
  When summer is outrun?
Where do the black-eyed tribes go back,
  The dwellers in the sun?

They'll never tell their secret,
  Never, to such as I!
For my demand they'll have at hand
  Some quick and pretty lie.
But sure as spring brings cuckoos
  Where winter brought us none,
The black-eyed train will come again
  Following the sun.

OCTOBER 11
'Whither are we Straying?'

IN the autumn of 1837 George Borrow was in Spain, where he fell in with the Zincali, the Gypsies, to whom he was drawn everywhere as a needle to the magnet. In Badajoz he made a friend of Antonio, a dark grim man of fifty, who would not have hesitated to stick a knife in a man, but never beat his mule. 'We are not cruel to our animals,' he said, 'our law forbids it. When I was a child I was beating a burra, but my father stopped my hand and chided me. "Hurt not the animal," said he, "for within it is the soul of your own sister." '

Borrow inquired, 'And do you believe in this wild doctrine, O Antonio?'

He answered, 'Sometimes I do, sometimes I do not. There are some who believe in nothing; not even that they live! Long since, I knew an old Caloro, he was old—very old, upward of a hundred years—and I once heard him say, that all we thought we saw was a lie; that there was no world, no men nor women, no horses nor mules, no olive trees. But whither are we straying?'

OCTOBER 12
COLUMBUS DAY

The Great Discovery

CRISTOFERO had a mind
Facts were powerless to bind.

He declared that he had seen
Mermaids sporting on the green,

And the world, he used to swear,
Was not an orange, but a pear.

Little wonder then that he,
Blown across the unknown sea

On the quest of far Cathay,
Lit upon the U.S.A.,

And while seeking for the Khan
Met his first Red Indian.

OCTOBER 13
'Wine-Month'

THE Romans called it October, or the Eighth Month, and by this time they seem to have lost poetry in naming their Calendar, and taken to numbers; for Gods and Heroes are no more enshrined in their month-names.

But the Saxons called it *Wyn-Monath*, or Wine-Month, not, it seems, because they themselves were making wines in October, but because other grape-bearing countries were. A lovelier name, perhaps the loveliest of all, was given to this month by the ancient Germans, who called it *Winter-fyllith*, because in this month the full moon marked the dawn of winter.

OCTOBER 14
WILLIAM PENN *born* 1644

'Such is the country of William Penn's settling!'

SUCH was William Cobbett's comment on Pennsylvania, in 1818, when he himself was settling to a period of farming life in America. This home-spun man, with his eye for what was good, and his love of what was sensible, was delighted with the American towns where there was nothing splendid and nothing beggarly; nothing too fine and nothing too poor; but a manner of life in which hard work, abundant living, and contentment seemed to go hand in hand. The modest farm-houses and the superb barns struck him especially in Penn's country:

'Barns of *stone*, a *hundred feet long* and *forty wide*, with two floors, and raised roads to go into them, so that the waggons go into the *first* floor up-stairs. . . . All about them looks so comfortable, and gives such manifest proofs of ease, plenty, and happiness!'

About the farm-houses, this plain-writing, plain-spoken man speaks poetry without knowing it:

'It is a curious thing to observe the farm-houses in this country. They consist, almost without exception, of a considerably large and very neat house, with sash windows, and of a *small house*, which seems to have been *tacked on* to the large one; and, the proportions they bear to each other, in point of dimensions, is, as nearly as possible, the proportion of size between a *Cow* and *her Calf*, the latter a month old. But, as to the *cause*, the process has been the opposite of this instance of the works of nature, for, it is *the large house which has grown out of the small one*. The father, or grandfather, while he was toiling for his children, lived in the small house, constructed chiefly by himself, and consisting of rude materials. The means, accumulated in the small house, enabled a son to rear the large one; and, though, when *pride* enters the door, the small house is sometimes demolished, few sons in America have the folly or want of feeling to commit such acts of filial ingratitude, and of real self-abasement. For, what inheritance so valuable and so honourable can a son enjoy as the proofs of his father's industry and virtue?'

OCTOBER 15
Fall of the Leaf

GILBERT WHITE of Selborne watched the fall of the leaf in his country-side, as he watched everything else. 'One of the first trees that becomes naked,' he tells us, 'is the walnut; the mulberry, the ash, especially if it bears many keys, and the horse-chestnut come next. All lopped trees, while their heads are young, carry their leaves a long while. Apple-trees and peaches remain green very late, often till the end of November: young beeches never cast their leaves till spring, till the new leaves sprout and push them off; in the autumn the beechen-leaves turn of a deep chestnut colour. Tall beeches cast their leaves about the end of October.'

He does not mention the elm; in Sussex, the next county to his Hampshire, I noticed that the elms kept their leaf without loss till mid-November, and shed them one day in the space of an hour. The down-rush of the leaves of a big elm was like the rush of rain or wings.

OCTOBER 16
A Tongueful of Sussex

LEAVES are falling, and good native words are dying out all over England, more's the pity. Here are some expressive words from the old Sussex dialect, which are falling more and more out of use—and the varied colour of the language falls with them.

A slovenly girl was a 'slocksey' girl, an irritable person was 'tessy and tiffy', and children's cheerful voices were 'gansing-gay'.

Then, 'popple'—the waves 'poppled' when the sea was like a boiling pot. Who hasn't seen a poppling sea?

A 'dezzick' was a day's work; 'bettermost' meant superior, and is, to my ears, superior to 'superior'. Mown grass was 'clung grass'; and thick greasy mud was 'slub', a much thicker and greasier word than 'slush'.

'She doddles to-and-again'—can't you see an old woman going about her room on unsteady feet? How pretty were the local words, 'Appleterre' and 'Applety', for orchard and apple-loft. 'Print-moonlight' was the bright moon you could read by; if you felt 'slap' you were in hearty health; and if you didn't catch a person's words, 'Quiddy?' you asked; as the first Norman landing at Hastings, on meeting his first Sussex-man, may have asked, 'Que dis?'

OCTOBER 17
The Whisper
(*A Russian Proverb Tale*)

A MOTHER and her child played together on a bench under a tree; the air was so still that the last pale rose on the wall did not stir. At the far end of the bench the old grandmother sat with her withered hands in her lap, smiling at the child's game. Presently like a sigh a dry leaf fluttered against the baby's cheek. Yet the day was windless. How had it detached itself from the twig overhead? For no other reason than that its time was ripe to fall. The child clutched at the leaf and crumpled it at his ear.

'Silly baby,' teased the mother fondly, 'silly baby! the yellow leaf can't talk.'

The grandmother said softly, 'The fall of a leaf is a whisper to the living'. And she looked into the autumn mist, where what she saw was close upon her. But the mother tossed her baby in the sun, where she saw the endless future in a vista of light.

OCTOBER 18
Now! says Time

Now! says Time,
and lifts his finger,
and the leaf on the lime
may not linger.
When Time utters
Now! and lifts

his finger, the oakleaf flutters
and drifts,
and elm and beech
let a leaf from the bough
when, finger lifted, to each
Time says *Now!*

OCTOBER 19
Autumn-Cleaning

THE wind blows, down come the leaves, and out comes
the man with a broom, to sweep up the litter all over
the earth. Spring-cleaning's a matter for women; but
autumn-cleaning is a job for giants. Princess Monice of the
Liverpool Zoo thinks so too, and in autumn she walks about
the grounds helping to sweep up the leaves with a birch-
broom in her—
Her hand?
No, her trunk. Princess Monice is an elephant.

When the poor little man with a broom was hurrying
all over the world, trying to be everywhere at once, the
Elephant stood up and addressed the animal kingdom.
'Brothers and Sisters! the October gales are upon us. The
earth is a mess of leaves. The fields are clogged with summer-
dirt. The hedges are too untidy for words. The clouds need
a touch of white-wash. The rose-hips want polishing, the
chestnuts want varnishing, the blackberries want black-
leading, and everything wants dusting. And Poor Little Man
has got to do it all! Look there.'

The animals looked, and saw Poor Little Man doing his level best.

'Go home, Little Man!' cried the animals in one breath. 'The house is your look-out, the earth is ours.'

Poor Little Man threw down his broom, and went home.

The Elephant curled her trunk round the broom-handle, and set to on the leaves.

The Giraffe stretched his neck, and fetched down the old nests from the elm-tops.

The Tree-toad put on shammy-leather gloves, and polished the nuts till you could see your face in them.

The Red Admiral passed his wings over the hips and haws, and left them glowing.

The Hedgehog became a wire-brush, and scratched the dirt out of the ditch.

The Razorbill trimmed the hedges as neat as neat.

The Spider hung new silk curtains up and down.

The Squirrel dusted high and the Fox dusted low with their brushes.

The white-winged gulls flew up and feather-dusted the clouds.

The Bat out-flew them, and breathed on the new moon, then rubbed off the mist till she shone like a looking-glass.

In short, all the world over the animals were busy autumn-cleaning.

Or did I dream it?

At least it is true that in autumn Princess Monice sweeps the leaves in the Liverpool Zoo with a broom in her trunk.

OCTOBER 20
To an Oak dropping Acorns

WITH my two arms I cannot span thy girth,
Yet when I pick thy acorn from the earth
Within my hand I hold a ship at sea,
My bed, my table, and my own roof-tree.

OCTOBER 21

TRAFALGAR DAY

LORD NELSON *died* 1805

A Medal for the Baker's Boy

THERE was once a Devonshire baker whose name was
Westcott, and he had a son who did not wish to follow
his father's trade. The baker's shop was in the little rustic
town of Honiton, far from the coast, yet somehow young
Westcott smelt the sea above the hot smell of bread in his
father's oven. So to sea the lad went. Being a poor boy, he
must have begun as a powder-monkey; and being a gallant
boy, he ended as a captain.

The baker died, and the baker's wife grew old. Mrs.
Westcott, living out her days in the Devonshire village,
counted time till her son came home to hug her between his
voyages and battles. Proud she must have been when he
became one of the great Nelson's captains, and took part in
his naval engagements.

Maybe it was in 1794 that Captain Westcott said: 'Well,
mother! in the fight off Calvi, Commander Nelson lost an
eye.'

[322]

Three years later perhaps he said: 'There, mother! we had a hot time round Cape St. Vincent, and Admiral Nelson lost his right arm.'

The year after that, in 1798, came a bigger sea-fight still, the Battle of the Nile. But after it was fought and won, Captain Westcott did not come home to Honiton to tell his mother that Admiral Nelson had been made a Lord.

One day, as the old woman sat at home, a visitor came to her door. He wanted an eye, and his right sleeve was pinned to the breast of his admiral's uniform; and Mrs. Westcott knew at once who it must be. Lord Nelson said that, finding himself near Honiton, he had wished to see the mother of Captain Westcott, who had died bravely in the Battle of the Nile, and he must have spoken words that warmed her heart. Then he went on to ask about the medal which her son had won in that battle, although he had not lived to receive it. Did it not comfort her to hold and look at it? But—

'No, sir,' said the old mother, 'nobody's never sent me my boy's medal'.

Then Lord Nelson unpinned his own gold medal from his uniform, and gave it to her to keep in her son's memory— 'I hope', he said, 'this is of no less value because I have worn it.'

She treasured it till she died, for her son's sake and Nelson's. If you go to Honiton, look for Captain Westcott's monument in St. Michael's Church. But where the medal is, I do not know.

OCTOBER 22

The Feast of the Full Moon

IN Burma Lent lasts for three months: from the end of July to the full moon in October. The rains are over, the time of telling 'Sorrow, Misery, Trouble' to the prayer-beads is ended; now the cool weather approaches, and gladness comes full with the moon. This is the greatest festival of the year, and is held at the Shwe Dagon pagoda at Rangoon. From the flat top of a little conical hill the gold cone of the pagoda tapers three hundred feet in air; the golden fretwork spire sparkles with jewels, and quivers like a flame in the radiant light. Below it, myriad little bells tinkle from the gold spires of the tiny shrines on the platform. A stairway leads up the hill to the little shrines. Up and down the stairs, passing all day, climb the old ones and the young ones, dressed in their best, in pink and green and purple silks, white striped with red, orange and indigo, rainbow silks, silks embroidered with silver. Gayest of all are the men's turbans and the girls' handkerchiefs. The old men climbing slowly, the old women chatting, the young men laughing gaily, the pretty girls murmuring sweetly, all are smiling, yet mindful of their reverences as they approach the great pagoda, pausing at the stalls on the way to buy sugar-cakes and rice, or jointed dolls, a silken garment or a satin turban, or gleefully watch the marionette shows and the dancers: while the bells ring brightly as the tongues of the stars which begin to prick the sky, and the crimson moon of autumn swims up through the mists, turning from red to gold, then silver, as it rises. Then chains and spots and circlets of red lights outline the shrines and spires and the great pagoda, little wicks float and flame in the lipped earthen jars of coco-nut oil.

And children? Yes, there are numbers and numbers of children, the small ones clinging to the bigger ones, and they, says one who once took part in this festival, are the only ones who do not laugh and smile. 'They are as gay as butterflies in their dress, but their looks are very solemn. There is no solemnity like that of a little child; it takes all the world so very seriously, walking along with great eyes of wonder at all it sees about it.'

OCTOBER 23
Old Wives' Fables for Pi-pos

COLERIDGE had a little boy, whom he called 'Pi-pos'. Charles Lamb said he was the only child, 'except a beggar's brat', that he had ever wanted to steal. He sent him books, of the sort he loved himself, and not the 'modern' books of 1802, when information was taking the place of imagination. In this year he wrote to Coleridge, on October 23:

'I am glad Pi-pos's books please. "Goody Two Shoes" is almost out of print. Mrs. Barbauld's stuff has banished all the old classics of the nursery; and the shopman at Newbery's hardly deigned to reach them off an old exploded corner of a shelf, when Mary asked for them. Mrs. B.'s and Mrs. Trimmer's nonsense lay in piles about. Knowledge insignificant and vapid as Mrs. B.'s books convey, it seems, must come to a child in the *shape* of *knowledge*,

[325]

and his empty noddle must be turned with conceit of his own powers when he has learnt that a Horse is an animal, and Billy is better than a Horse, and such like; instead of that beautiful Interest in wild tales which made the child a man, while all the time he suspected himself to be no bigger than a child. Science has succeeded to Poetry no less in the little walks of children than with men. Is there no possibility of averting this sore evil? Think what you would have been now, if instead of being fed with Tales and old wives' fables in childhood, you had been crammed with geography and natural history?'

OCTOBER 24

Scorpio

(*A Zodiac Song*)

SCORPION, like a lobster slipped
  Across its reef,
Within his fatal claw has nipped
  The yellow leaf,
He has come to sting the rose
  And blight the grass.
What wonder veiled October goes
  Sighing *Alas*.

OCTOBER 25

The Loyal Canary

'QUAH-QUAH!' said the Old Grey Goose to her goslings, 'stupid geese may be, which is a matter of opinion, but dumb they are not, which even canaries have been known to be, in token of which Charles Mordaunt that died on the twenty-fifth day of October in Seventeen-hundred-and-thirty-five, being Earl of Peterborough in the time of King James the Second, walked in his youth down the Charing Cross Road with a young lady on his arm that loved birds whereas Charles loved her, and "to prove it", said she, "be pleased to procure me the canary which sits singing so fine in its cage in that coffee-shop yonder, for I never heard a songster whistle so sweet", and it seeming an easy way to his inamorata's favours Charles goes in the shop and offers the mistress of the coffee-house a purseful of guineas for her canary, which the woman refused point-blank, laying young Mordaunt open to the fleers and jeers of his lady-love till he swore that by hook or by crook the bird should be hers, and never rested till he had found a canary the very spit of the other, except that it was as dumb as a fish, which, conveying to the coffee-house, he had the woman's attention diverted by sundry rakish customers while he made the exchange, and it is to be supposed his fair lady smiled upon him thereafter, but certain it is that King James was forced to fly the country for his life, while Charles Mordaunt, not being in the same predicament, continued to walk down the Charing Cross Road and presently took occasion to pop into the coffee-shop and mock at its mistress for having missed a good sale, vowing he would not now give a guinea for the bird, whereon, believe it or not, my goslings,' said the Old Grey Goose, 'the woman retorted, "and I would not part with the sweet creature for two pursefuls, since it has refused to utter a single note since our dear King was obliged to cross the water!" '

(*And this historic canary, you can take it from me, is as true as Alfred's cakes and Washington's cherry-tree, and possibly even truer.*)

OCTOBER 26
A Memory

THAT October morning
    Had a clear gold sun,
Round the turning trees
    A snow-white mist was spun,
In the quiet river
    The palest sky was seen,
Half the chestnut-fans
    Were yellow, half were green,
Soft were the dreams of autumn,
    Peace lay on the land,
When the fallow deer of Magdalen
    Fed from my hand.

OCTOBER 27

CAPTAIN JAMES COOK *born* 1728

Imaginary Conversation
between
Ben Yarner (aged 200) and Jack Robinson (aged 9)

JACK: I suppose you never knew Captain Cook, Mr. Yarner, did you?

BEN: Cap'n Cook? Course I knowed Jimmy Cook, as well as I knows you. Few years my elder were Jimmy. Yorkshireman. Born on a farm, in '28. They tried to make a farm-boy of Jimmy—but *that* wouldn't do. Then they tried to make him a grocer—and *that* wouldn't do neither. Preferred the sea to the sand, did Jimmy, and got hisself prenticed to Mr. Walker of Whitby, when he turned eighteen. Made his first trip in the *Freelove*, 450 tons.

JACK: What did he explore in her?

BEN: Newcastle to London and back agen. The *Freelove* were a coaling-ship. Never explored nothing to speak of till he turned forty. *Endeavour* Barque. Bound for the South Seas for to observe the Transit of Venus.

JACK: What's that?

BEN: Don't ask *me*. But 'Ben,' he sez, 'they've told me to go and observe Venus transitting, so come along and help.' We sails for Otaheite, where Queen Oberea made us welcome, after Jimmy had given her a little girl's doll. Which made her chief man, Tootahah, jealous; so we gave him a doll too. And they gave us a feast of bread-fruit and dog, which they baked in a hole in the ground; and there was music played on flutes, which the natives blew with their noses. Very affable they became, calling us by our names as best they could; they called Jimmy 'Toote'. Well, the best of friends must part. After Venus had done her little Transit, and been properly observed, off he goes agen; and in due course comes to Botany Bay. The natives there weren't so affable, but did that daunt Jimmy? He goes ashore, wags the Flag, and sez, 'I takes this coast in the name of Great Britain and King George the Third!' Then he turns to me and sez, 'Benjamin, this here place looks more like New South Wales to me than it do like Botany Bay.' 'You're right, James,' sez I. So New South Wales he renames it.

JACK: What did you do after that, Mr. Yarner?

BEN: More than'll go in a sailor's thimble. Good days they was, explorin' round the world with Cap'n Cook. Too bad he got hisself eaten on his third great voyage.

JACK: Sharks?

BEN: Sandwich Island Cannibals. There'd been a bit of a shindy. However! he'd been to the South Pole on his second voyage, so there wasn't much left for him to see in *this* world. That chocolate you're eating? They wraps it up watertight in tinfoil, don't they? Keeps out the weevil. Jimmy Cook were the first cap'n to line his food chests with tinfoil. Kept the biscuit eatable. That chocolate pretty eatable? Oh, thankee!

Captain Cook

OCTOBER 28

Autumn Sigheth

W IND bloweth,
Water floweth
Feather flieth,
Bird goeth.
Whither, bird?
Who can tell?
None knoweth . . .
Fare-well.

Wind bawleth,
Summer palleth,
Rose fadeth,
Leaf falleth.
Wither, leaf,
Where you fell,
Winter calleth . . .
Fare-well.

Tree turneth,
Bonfire burneth,
Earth resteth,
Sleep earneth.
Whither, earth?
To dream a spell
Till flower returneth . . .
Sleep well.

OCTOBER 29

JOHN KEATS *born* 1795

John Keats and little Fanny

'Sept. 10th (1817)

'My dear Fanny,

Let us now begin a regular question and answer—a little pro and con; letting it interfere as a pleasant method of my coming at your favourite little wants and enjoyments, that I may meet them in a way befitting a brother.

'We have been so little together since you have been able to reflect on things that I know not whether you prefer the History of King Pepin to Bunyan's Pilgrim's Progress— or Cinderella and her glass slipper to Moor's Almanack. However in a few Letters I hope I shall be able to come at that and adapt my scribblings to your Pleasure. You must tell me about all you read, if it be only six Pages in a Week.'

This was the first of a series of letters from John Keats to the little sister he hardly knew, because her guardians had placed her at some distance away, at a school in Walthamstow. The young poet put all sorts of sweet nonsense and gay advice into his letters, and set himself to waken Fanny's fancy with the legends he loved best. These were the words in which the child first heard of Endymion.

'Perhaps you might like to know what I am writing about. I will tell you. Many Years ago there was a young and handsome Shepherd who fed his flocks on a Mountain's Side called Latmus—he was a very contemplative sort of a Person and lived solitary among the trees and Plains little thinking that such a beautiful Creature as the Moon was growing mad in Love with him.—However so it was; and when he was asleep on the Grass she used to come down from heaven and admire him excessively for a long time; and at last could not refrain from carrying him away in her arms to the top of that high Mountain Latmus while he was a dreaming—but I dare say you have read this and all the other beautiful Tales which have come down from the ancient times of that beautiful Greece.'

He tells Fanny to let what she writes to him be a diary of her little life. 'You will preserve all my Letters and I will secure yours—and thus in the course of time we shall each of us have a good Bundle—which, hereafter, when things may have strangely altered and god knows what happened, we may read over together and look with pleasure on times past—that are now to come.' But Keats's 'time to come' was very short, for he died when he was only twenty-six.

OCTOBER 30
'Punkie Night'
(A Somersetshire Custom on this day)

HERE come children
On Punkie-night
With mangold-lanterns,
And candle-light
Gleaming inside
The goblin-faces'
Yellowy grins
And gold grimaces.

In and out
Of Hinton St. George,
By church and hostel,
By farm and forge,
Swinging their gargoyle
Mangolds bright,
There go children
On Punkie-night.

OCTOBER 31

Hallowe'en

ON Hallowe'en the old ghosts come
About us, and they speak to some;
To others they are dumb.

They haunt the hearts that loved them best;
In some they are by grief possessed,
In other hearts they rest.

They have a knowledge they would tell;
To some of us it is a knell,
To some, a miracle.

They come unseen and go unseen;
And some will never know they've been,
And some know all they mean.

NOVEMBER

NOVEMBER 1
Enter November

Here's November,
The year's sad daughter,
A loverless maid,
A lamb for the slaughter,
An empty mirror,
A sunless morn,
A withered wreath,
The husk of the corn,
A night that falls
Without a to-morrow,
Here's November,
The month of sorrow.

NOVEMBER 2

The Festa of the Santi

WHEN Randolph Caldecott was drawing English land-
scapes and figures for children's delight, a lady came
back from Italy with some pretty accounts of what she had
seen there, and set him drawing pictures of dark-eyed women
in head-shawls and coloured skirts, old straw-hatted priests
in vineyards, girls selling violets and camellias in decaying
marble palaces, blue bays set among mountains and cypress-
trees.

Amongst them is a delicate picture of the graceful yellow
chestnut groves in the Apennines, with little figures climbing
the tree-trunks and others stooping for the fallen nuts. It is
the time of the Festa of the *Santi*, which starts at the end of
October and goes on into November: the last great Festa
before Christmas comes. The chestnut-fans have a sunset
look, the nuts are ripe in their rough cases. The men shin
nimbly up the tallest trees, and thrash the nuts for the women
underneath, who shell and heap them into baskets which they
carry on their heads, into bags which weigh down their
shoulders. There are not many men; they are wanted in the
fields, and the chestnut harvest is the women's labour. At
dusk they lift their burdens and go home, each night to a
different cottage in the neighbourhood, where the men join
them. After a supper of *polenta* or *minestra*, the pot and chain
are taken off the fire and the chestnut-pan is brought for the
first roasting of the season. Chattering, laughing, singing,
flirting, cursing when the hot nuts burn their fingers, they

Y   [337]

sit in the red firelight night after night, during the three weeks of the chestnut-harvest, eating their fill and spreading the open rafters of the kitchen with the nuts which, dried and ground, are the poor Italian's flour.

NOVEMBER 3
A Bag of Chestnuts

THE chestnut man is in the street
With his glowing cave of heat.
He makes my hurrying footstep lag,
And takes my twopence for a bag.

Once more into the London cold
I turn my face.   But as I hold
The hot brown nuts between my hands,
My heart is gone to other lands.

Were these the English squirrel's food?
Did they come from Rewel Wood,
Or any other wood that crowns
Some high curve of the Sussex Downs?

Or does the tree that bore them bear
The velvet-eyed Italian's fare,
And swelled they in the light that shines
On peasants in the Apennines?

I do not know; but I shall know
As soon as I dip in, and go
Tasting beneath the London sky
My England or my Italy.

NOVEMBER 4
Little Ones' Bonfires

WHEN Goethe was an old man he saw in children, and their games and their pleasures, signs of the ever-lasting, because they were always the same and always being renewed. 'I need only look out of the window,' he said, 'to see in the brooms that sweep the street, and the children who run about, a visible symbol of the world: always wearing out, and always becoming young again. Children's games and diversions are preserved from century to century; trivial as these may appear to the mature, children are always children, and at all times alike. So we ought not to put down the bonfires, or spoil the pleasure which the little ones take in them.'

NOVEMBER 5

GUY FAWKES DAY

Blowing up Guy

IN 1839, when people were experimenting in all sorts of exciting ways with gas, Mr. Spence, a respectable solicitor of Pentonville, celebrated Guy Fawkes Day in an unusual manner. Instead of stuffing an old suit with straw and trundling it to the bonfire, he constructed a tissue figure of Guy twelve foot tall, blew it up with hydrogen, and let it loose from his grounds at the appropriate moment.

'This apparition, as it may be justly termed,' said one account, 'rose in a perpendicular manner, and the action of the wind upon the arms and legs gave it the effect of a person walking in the air. It caused an extraordinary degree of excitement as it passed over the city and crossed the river into Kent.'

I wish I had been there to see.

NOVEMBER 6

The Honest Jack Tars

EARLY in one November a fine French gentleman stood on the deck of the Swedish frigate *Freya* and saw the coast of Norfolk growing plainer. When the frigate lay as close to Yarmouth as she could, the boat's crew of H.M.S. *Majestic* put out to bring the fine gentleman ashore; sixteen honest, weather-beaten East Anglian salts, who took an order to be an order, d'ye see, and knew how to obey it. Well, and if so be their passenger chose to be addressed as the Count de

Lille, let him! it wasn't for the likes o' them to call him Your Majesty King Louis the Eighteenth of France. Mum's the word, but let the poor refugee see that British seamen know their manners.

The respect they showed him charmed the exiled king, who left behind him fifteen golden guineas, that the crew might drink his health.

Well, this puts the honest men in a pickle, d'ye see? For wasn't there an order in the Navy that British seamen must take no money from strangers? They held a confabulation and thrashed it out. And the end of it was they wrote this letter to Admiral Russell.

'*Majestic*, 6th day of November 1807.

PLEASE YOUR HONOUR,

We holded a talk about that there £15 that was sent us, and hope no offence, your honour. We don't like to take it, because, as how, we knows fast enuff, that it was the true king of France that went with your honour in the boat, and that he and our own noble king, God bless 'em both, and give every one his right, is good friends now; and besides that, your honour gived an order, long ago, not to take any money from no body, and we never did take none; and Mr. Leneve, that steered your honour and that there king, says he won't have no hand in it, and so does Andrew Young, the proper coxen; and we hopes no offence —so we all, one and all, begs not to take it at all. So no more at present.

'From your honour's dutiful servants.'

(*Signed*) 'Andrew Young, *Coxen*; James Mann; Lewis

Bryan; James Lord; James Hood; W. Edwards; Jan. Holshaw; Thomas Laurie; Thomas Siminers; Thomas Kesane; Simon Duft; W. Fairclough; John Cherchil; Thomas Laurence; Jacob Gabriel; William Muzzy.'

The Admiral's reply is not to hand; but I'll wager fifteen golden guineas he let those sixteen honest tars drink the French king's health, d'ye see?

NOVEMBER 7

Fortunes in Teacups

GOSSIPS sitting at their brew
Talk of death and birth and marriage.
Who will cross the water, who
Wed a lord and keep her carriage:
    Here's a purse,
    There's a letter,
    Some one's worse,
    Some one's better,
    Dark-eyed stranger
    Telling lies,
    Sudden danger,
    Big surprise,
    Broken heart,
    Storm at sea,
    Sweethearts part—
    Pour the tea!

Distant friend
Turning up,
Journey's end—
Fill the cup!
Kettle sings and crickets shrill,
Many things for good and ill,
Tea-leaf fortunes false and true,
Swim upon the gossips' brew.

NOVEMBER 8
The Wizard

WHEN the great traveller Kinglake was in Cairo, he wanted to see something of the Egyptian magicians. They were supposed to be wonder-workers, and might, he thought, be descendants of the wizards who had opposed 'the superior power of Aaron'. An old man was brought to him, dressed for his part: vast turban, flowing beard, and ample robes complete. With him was a small boy, whom he swore he had picked haphazard from the streets. By means of this child, said the wizard, he could show Kinglake the images of his friends.

A smoking pan of spiced charcoal was prepared; the room was clouded with sweet fumes; and the wizard stood over the embers muttering incantations, while with magic ink he wrote mystic characters on the little boy's palm.

'Look neither to right nor left,' he commanded the child. 'Look in your palm and tell us what you see.'

The boy answered tremblingly, 'I see a procession of flags and banners.' He described the procession in great detail.

The wizard seemed satisfied that the boy's eyes were in working-order, and turning to Kinglake said: 'Name the friend you desire this boy to describe to you.'

Kinglake thought of the oddest-looking man among his friends, the fierce, ill-humoured scholar Keate, whose appearance differed from every other human being; his red shaggy eyebrows were, says Kinglake, so prominent 'that he habitually used them as arms and hands for the purpose of pointing out any object towards which he wished to direct attention; the rest of his features were equally striking in their own way and were all and all his own; he wore a fancy-dress, partly resembling the costume of Napoleon and partly that of a widow-woman.'

'Whom do you name?'

'I name John Keate.'

'Now, what do you see?' said the wizard to the boy.

'I see,' answered the boy, 'I see a fair girl with golden hair, blue eyes, pallid face, rosy lips.'

Kinglake shouted with laughter. The dismayed wizard, seeing the shot had misfired, cried: 'None but the innocent can see the truth! this boy must have known sin!' And accordingly kicked him downstairs.

NOVEMBER 9

LORD MAYOR'S SHOW DAY

The Lord Mayor and the Lion

THE most famous of all Lord Mayors of London, Sir Richard Whittington, is remembered by his cat. Sir John Gayer, a less famous Lord Mayor in the reign of

Charles I, is associated with much bigger game. He went to Arabia and met a lion. His life was providentially spared, and thanking God he left the desert and returned to England, where lions are only to be met in cages. Nevertheless, Sir John in due course died.

Then it was found that his Will, dated 1648, provided for an annual Thanksgiving Sermon in the church of St. Katharine Cree. The 'Lion Sermon' was to be preached each 16th October, the date, I suppose, on which Sir John was spared. The custom still holds. Nearly three hundred 'Lion Sermons' have been preached in St. Katharine Cree, in gratitude for the delivery of death by lions of this Lord Mayor, long dead.

NOVEMBER 10

OLIVER GOLDSMITH *born* 1728

Oliver Goldsmith

OLIVER GOLDSMITH
Was careless and willing,
He'd write a sweet ballad
To sell for a shilling,
His wisdom was folly,
His labour was play,
He'd borrow a guinea
And give it away.

At school he was simple,
At college a dunce;
To earn bread-and-butter
He failed more than once;

So he whistled his way
Over many a land,
A hole in his pocket,
A flute in his hand.

In bloom-coloured breeches
And blue silken coat,
Tho' he talked like 'Poor Poll',
Like an angel he wrote;
The burst of an earthquake
Alarmed not his ears,
But the crack of a teacup
Reduced him to tears.

Oliver Goldsmith,
The day that he died
Samuel Johnson's
Stout heart-strings were tried;
'Poor Goldy!' said Garrick;
'Poor Goldy!' sighed Burke;
And Joshua Reynolds
Laid down his work.

Let rich men envy
The fellow who ends
Loved by his neighbours
And wept by his friends,
Like Oliver Goldsmith,
Careless and willing,
Whose life was a ballad
He sold for a shilling.

NOVEMBER 11

Memorial Garden (Canterbury)

THE grey cathedral towers
Rise up like solid dreams
Above the garth where flowers
The late rose on the wall,
And yellow fruit-leaves fall.

Upon the leaded panes
Of the great window there
Many a little square
Of flattened light gleams out
As though new-wet with rains.

And in the air about
The dreaming towers, the crows
Like loose dark leaves are blown
By the same wind that blows
The petals of the rose.

Summer and warmth are flown,
Life falls from tree and sky,
And still the grey dream stays,
The life of other days
That never will blow by.

And where the petals fall
In that Memorial
Garth to the Kentish dead,
Love will walk the ways
When the last leaf is shed.

[347]

NOVEMBER 12
'Wind-Month'

NOVEMBER, the ninth month for the Romans, was Wind-Month for the Saxons. As always, something urgent in the earth or air gave colour to the name by which they spoke of things, and in this month of gales their boats came in and were laid up for the winter.

But as well as Wint-Monath it was sometimes called Blot-Monath, or Blood-Month, because now they slaughtered the cattle and salted it for their coming needs. Though some think that sacrificial rites in practice at this time gave this name for the month its awful meaning.

NOVEMBER 13
ROBERT LOUIS STEVENSON *born* 1850
A Birthday Present

WHEN Robert Louis Stevenson was 41, he gave away his birthday to a little girl. This is how he did it, by deed of gift:

'In consideration that Miss Annie H. Ide, daughter of H. C. Ide, in the State of Vermont, U.S.A., was born out of all reason on Christmas Day, and is therefore out of all justice denied the consolation and profit of a proper birthday . . .

'And considering that I have obtained an age when I have no further use for a birthday of any description . . .

'I do hereby transfer to the said Annie H. Ide all and whole my rights and privileges in the thirteenth day of November, to have, hold, exercise and enjoy the same in the customary manner, by the sporting of fine raiment, eating of rich meats, and receipt of gifts, compliments, and copies of verse, according to the manner of our ancestors.'

Two years later Annie went to Samoa, where R. L. S. had gone to live and die, and on 13 November, now her birthday, not his, he gave her a Samoan birthday-party: Samoan songs, Samoan food, Samoan flowers. For nearly half a century Annie Ide, who became Annie Cokran, has kept her birthday on his birthday; each 13 November the Deed of Gift is read aloud; and she has bequeathed to one of her nieces the most real Birthday Present that was ever given to a little girl.

NOVEMBER 14
November's Song

I RESTORE the primal line,
Stark and sturdy, frail and fine,
    Of the Dryads in the sun.
Stripped to bone, in ranks they stand
With their root-grip on the land,
    Ghost no more, but skeleton.
Banks are thick with blackened mast,
Earth's redundancy is past.
    Let her rest. Her work is done.

NOVEMBER 15

'The Olde, Olde, Very Olde Man'

'QUAH-QUAH!' said the Old Grey Goose to her goslings, 'here's something hard to believe, yet try to believe it, for it is recorded in history itself that on the Fifteenth day of November One-Thousand-Six-Hundred-and-Thirty-five they buried in Westminster Abbey *The Olde, Olde, Very Olde Man* called Thomas Parr, that was born in Shropshire in the year One-Thousand-Four-Hundred-and-Eighty-three, which makes him one-hundred-and-fifty-two years old at the date of his death, and why not, say I, in this world of wonders, seeing that he wed his first wife at the green age of eighty, and his second wife at the ripe age of a hundred-and-twenty, and in the last year of his life was brought by the Earl of Arundel to see the King in London, borne all the way there in a two-horse litter, cared for by Lucye his daughter-in-law riding a-horse-back beside him, kept merry on the way by an antique-faced fellow called Jack the Foole, and conducted and paid for by Brian Kelly, his Lordship's own servant, by which means Old Parr came face to face with King Charles before he died, which happened very soon after, the journey being too much for him, and believe it or not, my goslings,' said the Old Grey Goose, 'when the King asked the ancient who had lived longer than other men what he had done more than other men, the old reprobate answered, "I did penance when I was a hundred years old", quah-quah!'

(*Which he did in a white sheet at the church-door in Alderbury in 1588, and may I do the same if that's a lie.*)

NOVEMBER 16
A Pound of Smoke

THIS month of fog and smoke brings to mind a bet made by Queen Elizabeth with the man who brought a new source of smoke into England. It must have been when she saw Raleigh puffing clouds out of his long tobacco-pipe that she asked him jestingly, 'And how much, Sir Walter, does a pound of smoke weigh?'

'So much, Your Majesty,' said Walter, 'or thereabouts.'

'And I say *so* much,' declared Bess, 'or thereabouts.'

'A stake on it!' laughed Raleigh; and Bess agreed.

But how prove it? Bess was a great queen, and Raleigh a great adventurer, but neither of them was a great scientist; for proof they chose a simple and seemingly infallible method. Raleigh fetched out a pound of his precious tobacco, which was well and truly weighed. Then they burned it to the last shred. Then they weighed the ashes. And finally they subtracted the weight of the ashes from the pound which the tobacco had originally weighed. The residue must be the weight of the vanished smoke, for there was the ash under their very eyes. Which of them won: whether Bess had to give Raleigh a new cloak, or Raleigh the Queen a new ruff: we don't know. But we know they were both of them wrong.

NOVEMBER 17

Philip Shallcross, the Eminent Quill Driver

PHILIP SHALLCROSS died, in the little Derbyshire town
of Wirksworth, on 17 November, 1787. We shouldn't
know anything about him but for his tombstone, which
veils his faults and praises one of his virtues in this inscription:

> 'Near this place lies the body of Philip Shallcross, once
> an eminent quill driver to the attorneys of this town, he
> died the 17 of Novr 1787: aged 67. Viewing Philip in a
> moral light the most prominent and remarkable features
> in his character were his real and invincible attachment to
> dogs and cats, and his unbounded benevolence towards
> them as well as towards his fellow creatures.'

It was Charles Lamb who, reading the inscriptions in a
churchyard with his sister Mary, asked: 'Where be all the
bad people buried then, Mary?' And it is not often that you
see a fault even hinted at in these brief obituaries; that the
eminent quill driver had them seems evident from the
reference to the 'moral light', and from the rhymed lines
which follow:

TO THE CRITIC

Seek not to shew the devious paths Phil trode
Nor draw his frailties from his dread abode.
In modest sculpture let this tombstone tell
That much esteem'd he liv'd and much regretted fell.

What devious path? what frailty? Was Phil a little too
fond of his glass? We will not ask. Without pretending he

was perfect, his stone leaves us loving him for his invincible attachment and unbounded benevolence toward dogs and cats. For that let all else be forgiven him.

NOVEMBER 18

Cats

CATS sleep
 Anywhere,
Any table,
Any chair,
Top of piano,
Window-ledge,
In the middle,
On the edge,
Open drawer,
Empty shoe,
Anybody's
Lap will do,
Fitted in a
Cardboard box,
In the cupboard
With your frocks—
Anywhere!
They don't care!
Cats sleep
Anywhere.

NOVEMBER 19

CHARLES I *born* 1600

The Royal Spaniel's Rights

A SPECTACLED citizen of middle age received his summons not long ago to serve on the jury in the court of the Lord Chief Justice. He attended for several days without being called, and at last, when Lord Hewart took his seat, stood up and protested. Under his arm he carried a King Charles spaniel.

'I am fed up,' he said. 'I have been here every day this week. Are you not going to call me? I have brought my dog with me to-day, and I have been told that dogs are not allowed here. But let me tell you that a King Charles spaniel has a right to go to the Privy Council, and if it scratches at the door of Buckingham Palace, it must be let in.'

'Remove this man,' Lord Hewart directed.

'England for England,' declared the elderly citizen, 'that's me!' And he left the court with his spaniel under his arm.

[354]

NOVEMBER 20
The General
(*An Italian Proverb Tale*)

AT the end of a war a day was appointed to do honour to the victorious General. He rode on his black horse through the wide streets of the city on his way to the cathedral, where a Thanksgiving Service was to be held. Flags flew, bells pealed, the way was lined with people. In the middle of the road the military pageant moved like a red-and-gold river. The excited crowd did not see men, they saw only one man; the rest were merged into a band of bright colour and flashing metal, the setting for the General, the General!

'A great man, our General!' cried a fellow in the crowd.

'He has the brains!' said another.

'And what valour!' said a third.

'He has saved the nation,' declared a fourth. 'If he had been a lesser man, where would we be now?'

The crowd took up the shout: 'A great man! a great man! the General!'

In the crowd there were many women; some with wet eyes, because they could not finish weeping, some dry-eyed because they would never weep again. These women did not shout, they did not see the One Man in the procession. But as the red river streamed by, each saw one man, and he was generally a common soldier. The red band in the road was his setting, it seemed to flow from his body, from the wound of which he had died, of which millions of him had died. None shouted 'A great man!' for him. It is the common soldier's blood that makes the General great.

[355]

NOVEMBER 21
The Triumph

THEY are taking him through the town
   To the sound of drums,
And their shouts the trumpets drown:
   Here he comes!
But for the blood we shed,
   But for our throes,
They might be shouting instead:
   There he goes.

NOVEMBER 22
How the King of England Went to War

WHEN King Edward the Third went to war in France,
he pitched his banner upon a high bush, and sat in a
crimson pavilion, while the minstrels played and the clarions
sounded. Behind came the carts with tents and pavilions,
and mills to grind the King's corn, and forges to shoe his
lords' horses: six thousand carts, drawn by twenty-four
thousand stout horses. Some of the carts bore boats of boiled
leather, each able to hold three fishermen to catch the King's
supper wherever they found a lake or a pond to fish in; and
thirty falconers on horseback came on with their hawks, and
sixty couple of hounds and sixty of greyhounds; so that no
day passed but the King had his pleasure in hunting and
fishing. And while he and his barons sat feasting, the common soldiers had to forage for whatever food they could get.

The General

Meredith W. Hawes.

NOVEMBER 23

Sagittarius

(*A Zodiac Song*)

THE Archer draws his bow,
  Oh he draws his windy bow,
His starry-pointed arrows
  Shooting high, shooting low;
But none can find a feather
  Of the shafts he lets fly,
For the wild windy weather
  Whirls them low, whirls them high.

NOVEMBER 24

The Footmarks

TWO thousand years ago a Roman dog ran through the
yard where they were busy making tiles; and somebody
else ran too. Who was the dog? Who was Somebody Else?
And how do we know to-day that they ran there then?

In the Haunted Field near Angmering, in Sussex, a splendid
Roman Villa was being uncovered a few Novembers ago.
This two-thousand-year-old palace must have belonged to a
very great lord, for there were at least a dozen dressing-rooms
round his huge bath-house, with its two hot bath-chambers,
its warm bath, and its cold bath. One bath had a pink floor,
others were laid with mosaic in countless coloured stones,
and thousands of Roman tiles went to the building of the
Villa. On one of these tiles lie six prints from the paw of a
dog, and in another is embedded the print of a sandalled foot.
These prints could only have been made before the tiles

[358]

hardened, and that is how we know that the dog and Some-body Else ran over them, some two thousand years ago, when they were being made in Italy before they were sent to Britain.

'Pater!'

'Quiet there, Lucretia! I am busy.'

'You're only polishing your shield. I want to ask questions.'

'You ask too many questions. Go and play with Caesar.'

'Caesar's only a dog.'

'Caesar's the greatest man in the world.'

'When are you going with him to Britain again?'

'That's as the Fates decide.'

'Will you take me with you?'

'No, I will not.'

'Please, Pater, *please.*'

'That's enough, Lucretia, Run away.'

'I'll run away to Britain, then, with Caesar!' cried Lucretia. She whistled to her dog and darted off to watch the men in the tile-yard.

'Careful now, puella!' one of them warned her. 'The tiles are still soft. Where are you going so fast?'

'To Britain, to Britain!' sang Lucretia merrily. 'Look, I have landed!' And out of pure mischief she stepped on the man's last tile, while Caesar ran swiftly over his last-but-one.

'Canem, be off!' growled the workman. 'There are two good tiles spoilt. Oh well, I'll let 'em harden and go as they are. They'll never be noticed in Britain among the lot. . . .'

Perhaps that's how it was. Perhaps Lucretia, with Caesar at her heels, ran, and still runs, in Britain after all.

NOVEMBER 25

Catherinette

(On St. Catherine's Day in Paris unmarried girls over a certain age are said to be 'Capped by St. Catherine'. These 'Catherinettes' wear demure lace caps as they walk in the streets.)

CATHERINETTE,
Who never has yet
Been married or kissed,
Think what you've missed!

Crown your sweet face
With a bonnet of lace,
And walk in the city
So prim and so pretty.

Then some laughing lad
Will say 'It's too bad
Nobody's led her
To altar and wed her'—

And before you can speak
He'll kiss your fair cheek
For fancy or fun,
And if you don't run,

Or tremble or faint,
The cap of the Saint
You may soon lay aside
For the veil of the bride.

NOVEMBER 26
The Cranes Fly

THE crane is almost a legendary bird in Great Britain, where it can only be seen in the zoo. Even in Hungary, whose national bird it is, it may presently become a fairy-tale, for, like our own buzzard, it is growing rarer and rarer. Imagine, then, the surprise of the people in Buda-Pesth when one November, not long ago, the sky grew dark with cranes. Fifty or sixty flocks, each flock containing seventy birds, passed over the Hungarian capital, flying from no one knew whence to no one knew whither. It took this cloud of cranes four hours to cross the city. Such a sight had never been seen in Buda-Pesth before.

NOVEMBER 27
THANKSGIVING DAY
(The last Thursday in November)
American Hospitality

ON Thanksgiving Day, even more than at Christmas, the American tables groan. It is their greatest feast-day.

The Puritans who first sailed to America banished the Christmas festival as something Popish, and replaced it with a Thanksgiving Day for the Lord's bounties. In England the Puritan Oliver Cromwell had banished not only Christmas puddings but such frivolities as holly, maypoles, and play-actors. But the Americans did not go as far as this. If they could not have Christmas, they must have their own feast to satisfy their sense of hospitality.

American hospitality has always been famous. William Cobbett was struck by it when he went to live there, and contrasts his treatment with that of a guest in England.

'It is not with a little bit of dry toast, so neatly put in a rack; a bit of butter so round and small; a little milk pot so pretty and so empty; an egg *for you*, the host and hostess *not liking eggs*. It is not with looks that seem to say, "don't eat too much, for the tax-gatherer is coming". It is not thus that you are received in America. You are not much *asked*, not much *pressed*, to eat and drink; but, such an abundance is spread before you, and so hearty and so cordial is your reception, that you instantly lose all restraint, and are tempted to feast whether you be hungry or not. And, though the *manner* and *style* are widely different in different houses, the *abundance* every where prevails. This is the strength of the government: a happy people: and no government ought to have any other strength.'

NOVEMBER 28

Everyday Word-Meanings: HOSPITAL

I HOPE your home is a Hospital—'Hospital!' do I hear you cry. 'I live in a house, I'm not ill—why should you want me to live in a hospital?' Let us dig into the word a little, and see; we may bring a number of ideas to light as we turn it over and find, in the end, that everybody's house should be a kind of hospital.

To begin with: every house that is worth its salt is hospitable. It isn't only your father who is a host when he shows hospitality to Mr. Brown by asking him in for a smoke and a game of cards; you are just as much Master Brown's host when you ask him in for ping-pong and lemonade. The real meaning of a host is 'one who entertains guests'.

It meant something very real in the old days, when the innkeeper was spoken of as 'Mine Host' by the guests who paid for his entertainment, and received, over and above their food and lodging, the warm hospitality which cannot be paid for. Even the guests' horses had their 'host' in the stables: the ostler who looked after them, and was first spelt 'hostler' or 'hosteller'. He sometimes stole their oats, for his own profit, as his master sometimes cheated a guest—bad hosts these, showing very poor hospitality to man and beast.

From the hostel where Mine Host entertained his guests, we step at last to the hospital which simply meant a building for receiving guests. To-day it means only a building for receiving sick people as guests; and when we speak of a building for receiving travellers as guests, we call it an hotel. But hotel and hospital are one and the same word.

[363]

So I hope your home is a hospital in the best sense of the word. Just as innkeepers should be hospitable, or show kindness, to travellers: and doctors and nurses should be hospitable, or show kindness, to invalids: so you should be hospitable, or show kindness, to the guests who enter the door of the house you live in.

NOVEMBER 29

SIR PHILIP SIDNEY *born* 1554

'The Jewel of my Dominions'

THIS was how Queen Elizabeth described Sir Philip Sidney, high praise in an age when the finest minds England has ever known were thinking and writing, and the most adventurous spirits were daring and doing. Sidney did something of everything; he could govern a city, lead an army, set a fashion, and write a sonnet. But it was his character, more than any deed or poem, that made him the jewel of Elizabeth's court; he was born a nobleman, and was a noble man. He was a courtier, but never a flatterer, and risked the Queen's displeasure by speaking his mind. The end of his short life (he died just before he was 32) is one of the famous anecdotes in history. When he was lying mortally wounded on the battlefield of Zutphen, he gave up to a dying soldier the precious bottle of water brought to slake his thirst, without touching a drop of it. If you know no more of him than this, it sums up his character, and his words, 'This man's necessity is greater than mine', might almost come out of the Bible. But in his works and letters he said many other things worth remembering. 'Men are loving creatures,' he wrote, 'when injuries put them not from their natural course'; and 'As the love of heaven makes one heavenly, the love of virtue virtuous, so doth the love of the world make one become worldly'. These are words from the religious side of Sidney's nature; but he could be very human too. 'No remembrance of naughtiness delights me but mine own,' he confesses in a letter. And here's a fine line from one of his sonnets, which he himself lived up to:

'Fear is more pain than is the pain it fears.'

For Sidney did not write one thing and live another. 'Looke in thy heart and write,' he says in another poem, and he followed his own advice. He did more; he looked in his soul and lived, so that his life shone like a lovely influence upon his times, and after them. He might have been writing his own epitaph when he penned the line:

'We live short while, and build long-lasting places.'

NOVEMBER 30
At Eventide

WHEN the day has ended,
Do not sleep, oh do not sleep
Till your prayers have tended
All who laugh and all who weep.

Let your prayers like swallows
Eastward roam and westward roam,
Then, before sleep follows,
Bring them home, oh bring them home.

Flying all together,
Or alone, oh flying lone,
They will drop a feather
On the known and the unknown.

When your love has tended
All who laugh and all who weep,
And your prayers are ended,
Fall asleep, oh fall asleep.

DECEMBER 1

Boughs are Bare

BOUGHS are bare on Christmas Night,
But the windows flower with light,
Leaves of snow fall down the air
Even when the boughs are bare.
Somewhere on the earth's cold breast
Blooms the Rose that's loveliest.

DECEMBER 2

Winter-time

'A FROST that makes us jump and skip about like larks.'
So William Cobbett wrote in his journal, in his first
experience of an American winter. 'Very seasonable for a
sluggish fellow.' He couldn't have meant himself; one of his
tests of character was the will to get up early; a late riser, he

maintained, never caught up with himself through the day, or made good the hours lost at dawn. He had to be busy enough preparing for winter on the farm he had taken. He was always practical about country life, and the best ways of doing things well. This is what he did and how he did it.

'Patched up a boarded building, which was formerly a coach-house; but, which is not so necessary to me, in that capacity, as in that of a *fowl-house*. The neighbours tell me that the poultry will roost out on the trees all the winter, which, the weather being so *dry* in winter, is very likely; and, indeed, they *must*, if they have *no house*, which is almost universally the case. However, I mean to give the poor things *a choice*. I have *lined* the said coach-house with *corn-stalks* and *leaves of trees*, and have tacked up cedar-boughs to hold the lining to the boards, and have laid a *bed of leaves* a foot thick all over the floor. I have secured all against dogs, and have made ladders for the fowl to go in at holes six feet from the ground. I have made pig-styes, lined round with cedar-boughs and well covered. A sheep-yard, for a score of ewes to have lambs in spring, surrounded with a hedge of cedar-boughs, and with a shed for the ewes to lie under, if they like. The oxen and cows are tied up in a stall. The dogs have a place, well covered, and lined with corn-stalks and leaves. And now, I can, without anxiety, sit by the fire, or lie in bed, and hear the North-Wester whistle.'

DECEMBER 3
Silk Coats

(In China they reckon the weather by the number of silk coats you wear)

How many silk coats is to-day?
A hot day is a One-Coat-Day.
A warm day is a Two-Coat-Day.
A chilly day is a Three-Coat-Day.
A colder day is a Four-Coat-Day.
A frosty day is a Five-Coat-Day.
A freezing day is a Six-Coat-Day,
        a Seven-
        an Eight-
        or a Nine-Coat-Day.
How many silk coats is to-day?

DECEMBER 4
Onion-Coats

SPAIN in November watches its onion crop. By it they say they know whether it is to be a mild or a hard winter. Because when bitter weather is to be expected, Spanish Onions put on an extra coat, and double their brown outside wraps as a man in frosty weather puts on an extra cardigan.

DECEMBER 5

Musical Box

O N the 5th of December 1832, Miss Fanny Kemble sat in
her room at the Mansion House in Philadelphia, reading
a canto of Dante. The pretty actress, a niece of Mrs. Siddons,
was never left long alone in the cities where she and her
father had crossed the water to act, and soon she was 'called
down to see folk' and found the drawing-room 'literally
thronged'. Miss Kemble valued her privacy; but on this
occasion she must have forgiven her morning visitors, for
among 'a load of men' was one who had brought her 'a
curious piece of machinery, in shape of a musical box, to
look at. It contained a little bird, no larger than a large fly,
with golden and purple wings, and a tiny white beak. On
the box being wound up, this tiny creature flew out, and
perching itself on the brink of a gold basin, began fluttering
its wings, opening its beak, and uttering sundry very melodi-
ous warblings, in the midst of which, it suddenly sank down,
and disappeared, the lid closed, and there was an end. What
a pity', sighs Miss Fanny to conclude with, 'that we can only
realize fairyland through the means of machinery. One
reason why there is no such thing left as the believing faculty
among men, is because they have themselves learnt to make
magic and perform miracles'.

DECEMBER 6

ST. NICHOLAS DAY

Purses of Gold

THERE was a poor man of Patara with three young daughters to whom he could give no marriage portions. It seemed they must be thrown on the hard world. One moonlight night as he sat sorrowing for their fate, a purse of gold came flying through the window, sufficient for his eldest daughter's dowry. The following night a second purse was thrown, the second daughter's portion. The third night the man hid outside the house to catch the generous purse-thrower. He came in the flowing robes of a bishop. The man caught at his skirts saying: 'Nicholas! Servant of God!' Nicholas put his finger to his lips and gave him the third purse for his youngest daughter. The good Saint preferred to bestow his gifts in secret.

Out of this legend grew the idea that St. Nicholas loved making presents to young people, and children began to leave their shoes outside their doors on St. Nicholas Eve. In the morning they were filled with sweets and toys—and who could have filled them but St. Nicholas?

DECEMBER 7

Christmas Stocking

WHAT will go into the Christmas Stocking
  While the clock on the mantelpiece goes tick-
    tocking?
An orange, a penny,
Some sweets, not too many,

[371]

A trumpet, a dolly,
A sprig of red holly,
A book and a top
And a grocery shop,
Some beads in a box,
An ass and an ox
And a lamb, plain and good,
All whittled in wood,
A white sugar dove,
A handful of love,
Another of fun,
And it's very near done—
A big silver star
On top—there you are!
Come morning you'll wake to the clock's tick-tocking,
And that's what you'll find in the Christmas Stocking.

DECEMBER 8
Spanish Gold

IN December 1937 Van Wiener, a Dutch engineer,
prepared to go treasure-hunting in Tobermory Bay.
Two-and-a-half million pounds went down in one of the
richest Spanish galleons of the Armada, when Queen Elizabeth's seamen sent it flying round the coast. The Spanish
Dons did themselves very well; they ate off gold and silver
plate, and their heavy pay-chests were crammed with pieces
of eight. When a galleon sank, a king's ransom went down
with it. For three-hundred-and-fifty years divers have been

after that particular treasure-ship in Tobermory Bay. How came it to sink there?

The Maclean, Chief of the Isle of Mull, was at loggerheads with the Chiefs of the Isles of Muck and Rum. He had plenty of stores, but not enough men, for his quarrels.

'Chief,' said Donald Glas to him one day, 'there's a strange proud ship come into Tobermory Harbour, and her captain wants a word with you.'

'Let him have it,' said The Maclean, and went to speak with the commander of the galleon.

'Who may you be?' he asked.

'A foe to Queen Elizabeth of England,' the Don admitted.

'Hoots to that!' said The Maclean. 'I'm foe myself to the Chiefs of Muck and Rum.'

'I need stores,' said the Don.

'And I need men,' said The Maclean. 'Come, a bargain! I'll send stores for your ship if you'll lend men to fight those dastards of Rum and Muck.'

'A bargain!' agreed the Don.

The Maclean sent the stores, and the Don lent the men. These same fought and settled The Maclean's quarrels for him. After which, they wanted to get back to their ship; but——

'Not so fast,' quoth The Maclean. 'I must first be paid for my stores in pieces of eight.'

This message angered the Don. He held that the stores had been paid for by his men's services. But he hid his anger under a smile, twirled his moustachios, and said to the messenger: 'My compliments to your Chief, and tell him to send back my soldiers with a Highlander of Mull to collect the money for the stores.'

'Good!' said The Maclean. 'Go you, Donald Glas.'

Donald Glas put out with the Spanish soldiers, and came aboard the galleon.

'Where's that gold?' asked he.

'In the hold,' laughed the Don, 'and there it will stay.' And he gave the order to set sail.

That put Donald Glas in a fine temper. 'Let her have it!' cried he, and then and there he fired the powder-magazine. Down went the ship, Don, Donald, and all. And two-and-a-half million of Spanish gold was sunk in Tobermory Bay.

DECEMBER 9
No Sneezing at Court!

WHEN Miss Fanny Burney, the famous young authoress of *Evelina*, was Maid of Honour to Queen Charlotte in the Court of George III, she found that there were strict rules of behaviour for courtiers who dared to catch a cold. One December, when she had evidently suffered from the rules more than from the cold, she wrote to Mrs. Burney from Windsor, 1785, the following:

*'Directions for coughing, sneezing, or moving,
before the King and Queen.*

'In the first place, you must not cough. If you find a cough tickling in your throat, you must arrest it from making any sound; if you find yourself choking with the forebearance, you must choke—but not cough.

'In the second place, you must not sneeze. If you have a vehement cold, you must take no notice of it; if your nose-membrane feels a great irritation, you must hold your breath; if a sneeze still insists upon making its way, you must oppose it, by keeping your teeth grinding together; if the violence of the repulse breaks some blood-vessel, you must break the blood-vessel—but not sneeze.

'In the third place, you must not, upon any account, stir either hand or foot. If, by chance, a black pin runs into your head, you must not take it out. If the pain is very great, you must be sure to bear it without wincing; if it brings the tears into your eyes, you must not wipe them off; if they give you a tingling by running down your cheeks, you must look as if nothing was the matter. . . . . If, however, the agony is very great, you may, privately, bite the inside of your cheek, or of your lips, for a little relief; taking care, meanwhile, to do it so cautiously as to make no apparent dent outwardly. And, with that precaution, if you even gnaw a piece out, it will not be minded, only be sure either to swallow it, or commit it to a corner of the inside of your mouth till they are gone—for you must not spit.'

DECEMBER 10

One of These Days

(*A Serbian Proverb Tale*)

JUST before Christmas a little boy and his uncle went to tea with a little girl and her aunt. The aunt, a very voluble person, talked to the uncle downstairs, while upstairs the children took it turn by turn.

The little girl said, 'I'm going to the pantomime.' 'When?' 'One of these days, aunty says. It's a promise. Hasn't your uncle promised to take you to the pantomime?' 'No.' 'My aunty's promised me a dog for Christmas. What has he promised you?' 'He never promises me anything.' 'How mean! I'm going to marry a prince, one of these days.' 'How d'you know?' 'Aunty's promised it.'

When it was time to go the little boy was feeling discontented. The little girl's life was going to be so full of wonders always, and even to-morrow his had nothing to show.

They met again after Christmas. The little boy said, 'Wasn't it a gorgeous pantomime!' The little girl said, 'Was it?' 'Uncle took me yesterday, all of a sudden.' 'Aunty's going to take me one of these days.' 'Uncle gave me a terrier. What's your dog like?' 'One of these days I'm going to have a Great Dane.' But the little girl didn't look very contented. *Would* she, one of these days, marry a prince?

When they went away the uncle gave the little girl sixpence without a word, and suddenly she felt as happy as a queen.

Give to a child but promise him nothing, they say.

DECEMBER 11
Piecrust

SHALL I promise you the moon
And the mermaid's tune?
Or give you a ball
And the blackbird's call?
Shall I promise you the gold
In the rainbow's hold?
Or give you without any
Promise a penny?

> *More than your prayers*
> *In a promise may be spoken.*
> *Promises are piecrust*
> *Made to be broken.*

DECEMBER 12
Sixpence to Spend

SPENDING sixpence to the best advantage is a matter of
moment, especially in December. If this is your problem
now, it's none of my business whether you spend it on a
present for yourself or for somebody else. But I am quite
sure you won't spend it like the little boy in a story-book old
enough to have been read by your great-grandfather when
he was a little boy.

The little boy in the story had sixpence to spend. He
longed for—what do you think? A second-hand Horace.
Yes, and there was the very Horace, priced sixpence, in the

second-hand bookseller's. And instead of that, this horrid child spent his sixpence on—what do you think? Prawns for his mother.

Well, I hope that story did your great-grandfather good.

DECEMBER 13
There were Fairies in Wales

E LIDORUS, a Welsh priest in the twelfth century, swore that this had befallen him at the age of twelve. He was being instructed for the priesthood by severe methods, and to escape the discipline and stripes of his teacher he ran away and hid in a hollow in the river-bank. Here he remained without food for two days, when two pigmies appeared to him and said: 'If you will come with us, we will lead you into a country full of delights.'

Elidorus followed them through a subterranean tunnel, and came out from the darkness into a beautiful land rich in rivers and woods and meadows, but lit with a light that did not come from the sun; the pigmies' day was dim, and their night without stars. The youth was brought before the pigmy king and his court and given as a companion to the king's son, a boy like himself. The pigmies, said Elidorus, were all of tiny stature, beautifully proportioned; of fair complexion, with long luxuriant hair, both men and women. They had horses and hounds fitting to their size; ate no flesh, but lived on milk and saffron; and never took an oath, because they detested lies above all things. They had no other form of religion than their reverence for the truth, and scorned the ambitions, falsehoods, and infidelities of men. Their hemisphere abounded in gold.

Elidorus remained for some time among them, but often came back to his own hemisphere to see his mother, to whom he described the race he lived with and the place he lived in. One time she asked him to bring her a golden present on his next visit, and on his return he stole the gold ball he and the king's son played with, and fled to his own world with it, pursued by the two pigmies who had first found him. In his haste he stumbled at his mother's threshold, fell, and dropped the ball; the pigmies snatched it up and departed, with scorn and mockery. When he had recovered from his fall, he tried, full of shame, to return to the lower hemisphere; but though he sought for a year, he never found again the cave which led to the subterranean passage. In time the edge of sorrow was worn away, he resumed his learning, and became at last a priest; but even then could never speak of these things without shedding tears.

DECEMBER 14

Stirring the Pudding

STEM the currants, stone the raisins,
  Chop the peel as fine as fine,
Beat the eggs and shred the suet,
Grate the crumbs (no flour in mine!)
Freely shake, to make it nice,
All the virtues of the spice,
Pour the brandy liberally—
Stir and wish then, three times three.

He who finds the silver shilling
Fortune favours—drop it in;
She who finds the ring of silver
To the altar soon will win;
Let the lucky horseshoe fall,
Drop the button last of all—
Whoso finds, unwed will be.
Stir the pudding three times three.

Take the wooden spoon and ply it,
Stir the pudding strong and well,
Keep your stirring-wish unspoken,
What it is to no man tell.
Whether you a joy would gain,
Or demand the end of pain,
If fulfilment you would see,
Stir in silence, three times three.

DECEMBER 15
A Christmas Party

IN a Christmas Party, given in December 1937, there was:
A Christmas-tree hung with carrots and beetroot and bones.
A Christmas cake decorated with Brussels sprouts.
Places laid for Forty Guests.
Twenty Distinguished Visitors looking down from a box.
A sled led by Father Christmas and drawn by two Shetland
Ponies.
A banner saying

'P. D. S. A. wishes all a Merry Christmas!'

P. D. S. A. is the People's Dispensary for Sick Animals of
the Poor. The party was given in the yard of the Sanatorium
at Ilford. The Forty Guests were horses and ponies of all
sorts. The Distinguished Visitors were the dogs of the
Society's patrons. They barked a welcome as the horses took
their places round the table, some lame, some old, some tired,
but all well cared for. Here is Jimmie, the trace-horse from
Tower Hill, who works so hard all the week that he comes
to Ilford for a week-end rest-cure. Here is Duchess, the
Society's Shetland mascot, 15 years old; here's the Society's
baby, a Shetland pony of 3. And here is 27-year-old Pompey,
a war veteran, said to have been a Canadian gun horse. He
has forgotten the guns while he munches his Christmas
carrot.

When the Horses' feast is done, twenty platters are placed
on the table, and the Twenty Distinguished Visitors leap
yelping to their places. Human beings wait upon dogs and
horses. And somewhere in the Animals' Paradise, an Ox
and an Ass smile down on the Christmas Party.

DECEMBER 16

WILHELM GRIMM *died* 1859

Happily Ever After

WILHELM GRIMM and his elder brother Jakob were as learned as they were fanciful, and as attached to each other as the Siamese Twins. They lived and worked together all their lives, and the story of how this pair of bachelors went courting the same lady reads like one of their own fairy-tales.

They had an aged aunt who looked after them and their house and their clothes and their money. To her these wise professors were a couple of babes; she was sure the absent-minded old fellows weren't fit to look after themselves, and as she couldn't live for ever she insisted that marriage was the only thing for it. Neither Jakob nor Wilhelm liked the idea at all, but she dinned it into them till they gave in—on one condition.

'There is no need for both of us to marry,' they pointed out; 'let one be married and the other be spared. A single wife is quite enough to look after the pair of us.'

Old Aunt Grimm went ahead with it, and settled on a charming young lady as a suitable bride. Then the question arose: which of the two brothers should sacrifice himself? They argued about it for a week, until Jakob decided that, as the elder, it was his duty to go courting. But how *did* one go courting? Easy enough to make the prince woo the princess in a fairy-tale, but one's own courtship was another matter. 'My dear fellow,' he confided to Wilhelm, 'I haven't a notion how to do it, and the mere thought of it covers me with confusion.' Wilhelm, in the kindness of his heart, offered to pave the way for him, and began to visit the young lady in his brother's place—only to find himself as embarrassed as Jakob had been. Worse still, he began to suspect, to his horror, that the beautiful girl did not positively dislike him; and worst of all, that he did not positively dislike her. In short, by the end of the week, he was positively in love with her. He rushed in despair to his aunt, told her all, and groaned, 'What am I to do?'

'Tell her so,' said his old aunt very sensibly.

'I daren't!' whispered Wilhelm. 'And if I dared, don't you see that I am a traitor to my dear Jakob? He will never forgive me for what I couldn't help.'

'Booby!' said the old lady impatiently; and trotting off to Jakob she broke the news to him. Jakob dashed out of his study into Wilhelm's, and gripped him by the shoulders.

'*Ach*, Jakob!' cried the guilty young brother, 'how you must hate me!'

'Hate you!' cried the beaming elder brother. 'These are the most joyful tidings I ever heard!' Then, embracing Wilhelm, he whispered, 'I shall now go and hide in the Harz Mountains till you are safely married and the danger is past.'

He did so; the marriage was duly solemnized; and Wilhelm's wife looked after the two elderly brothers so well, that all three lived happily ever after.

DECEMBER 17
A Nursery Rhyme for Mr. Kemble

IN 1808 Covent Garden Theatre was burned down. In 1809 it was built up again.

In September it was opened to the public, with raised prices for the seats, because the superb new building had cost so much.

And for three months there wasn't a calm performance in the house, while Pit and Gallery yelled 'Old Prices! Old Prices!', and hooted Mr. John Kemble, the famous actor, and mewed at Madame Catalini, the great singer, until—

On 17 December Mr. Kemble signed a Treaty of Peace with his public, prices were lowered, and the 'O. P. Riots' came to an end.

But not before the O. P. Rioters turned up with speeches to spout at Mr. Kemble, and dances to stamp on the pit floor. Not before they wore hatbands proclaiming 'No HUMBUG FOR JOHN BULL!' Not before Mr. Kemble engaged Dutch Sam the prizefighter and several other pugilists to have free fights with the pittites and throw them out. And not before the newspapers printed a parody of the old nursery rhyme:

'This is the House that Jack built!
These are the Boxes, let to the Great,
That visit the House that Jack built!
These are the Poor in the Pigeonholes
Over the Boxes let to the Great
That visit the House that Jack built!'

And so on and so on, to the final verse:

'This is the Manager full of scorn
Who raised the Price to the People forlorn,
And directed the Thief-taker shaven and shorn
To take up John Bull with his Bugle-horn,
Who hissed the Cat engaged to squall
To the Poor in the Pigeonholes
    Over the Boxes,
      Let to the Great
Who visit the House that Jack built!'

DECEMBER 18

Yorkshire Christmas Pie

ACCORDING to 'A Lady' who, in 1760, wrote
THE ART OF COOKERY
MADE PLAIN AND EASY
Yorkshire Christmas Pies were favourite dainties to 'send
in a box as presents; therefore the walls must be well built'.
The walls were made of 'a good standing crust'; they took
a bushel of flour, and the contents were on the same Gar-
gantuan scale. They consisted of a 'turky', a goose, a fowl,
a partridge, and a pigeon. When they had been seasoned
with mace and nutmegs and cloves and salt and black pepper,
they were boned and opened all down the back, and the
pigeon was put into the partridge, the partridge into the
fowl, the fowl into the goose, and the goose into the 'turky,
which must be large, as it will look only like a whole turky';
after which you plumped your gobbler inside the crust and
garnished him with such small fry as a hare on the one side

and on the other 'woodcocks, moor game, and what sort of wild fowl you can get. Season them well, and lay them close; put at least four pounds of butter into the pie, then lay on your lid, which must be a very thick one, and let it be well baked.'

So if you want to send a Yorkshire Christmas Pie in a box for a Christmas present, you now know how to make it.

DECEMBER 19
Everyday Word-Meanings: LARDER

THIS is the time when Christmas puddings and Christmas pies, turkeys and geese, ribs of beef and crowns of pork, go into the larder; and this is a good moment to remember that, to begin with, a larder was nothing but a tub of lard.

Almost every larder has its jar of dripping; perhaps a bowl-ful, perhaps only a little saved in a broken cup. Cooks and mothers know the value of the last scraping of fat, as they knew it in the early days when language was making itself out of the conditions people lived in. There were then no special rooms or cupboards in which the peasants kept their stores. Their chief food came from their pig, and after the meat was hung up in the smoke, the precious fat was stored in a tub. This tub, which held the pig's lard, they called the larder.

In time the peasants' homes improved and even the poor ones had a cupboard, where not only the fat was kept but the meat; and the store-room kept the store-tub's name, and was still the larder. To-day your mother may ask you to go to the larder and bring the milk, the pudding, or the cold potatoes. But if you had been a young Anglo-Saxon sent to fetch what was in the larder, you would have found nothing to bring but lard.

DECEMBER 20
Pig!

M R. ALFRED FIELDSEND, of Tealby in Lincolnshire, had a wife and son.

He also had a pig.

A war-time pig, a bacon pig, not a pork pig. Bacon was to be rationed at 4 oz. per head per week, and pigs become pork when they weigh a mere 100 lb., while they cannot be bacon till they've gone on to 220. Mr. Fieldsend's pig was allowed to go on; it went on and went on and went on. It went from 250 lb. to 300 lb. It went from 350 lb. to 400 lb. It went from 450 lb. to 500 lb. And still it went on.

But the miller of Tealby stopped short. He sent word that there wasn't enough meal to satisfy this Gargantua who didn't know when a pig has had enough. So Mr. Fieldsend's pig had at last to become gammon and ham. It turned the scales at over a quarter of a ton; which, as Mr. Fieldsend observed, at the bacon-ration-rate, would last him, his wife, and his son, 12 years and 3 months.

DECEMBER 21
Menu for a King

THE Country was France. The Year, 1611. The King was ten years old. And this was what he had for dinner.
Corinth raisins in rose water.
Egg soupe with lemon juice, 20 spoonsful.
Broth, 4 spoonsful.
Cocks combs, 8.
A little boiled chicken.
4 mouthfuls of boiled veal.
The marrow of a bone.
A wing and a half of chicken, roasted and then fried in bread crumb.
13 spoonsful of jelly.
A sugar horn filled with apricots.
Half a sugared chestnut in rose water.
Preserved cherries.
A little bread and some fennel comfits.
The fennel comfits were for the little King's digestion.

DECEMBER 22

Mrs. Mapp

'QUAH-QUAH!' said the Old Grey Goose to her goslings, 'did you ever hear tell of Mrs. Mapp the Bone-setter of Epsom, whose tale is as true as twice-two-are-four, though it sounds like a pack of nonsense, for she wandered the country till she came to settle in Epsom-town, where she did wonder-working cures, more by luck than by skill, and married a Footman who made off with her savings, and that was the last of *him* and *Good Riddance!* quo' she, driving to town once-a-week in her smart coach-and-four, coming back with a coachful of crutches as a proof of the lame legs she'd cured, not to speak of the man she mended in the Grecian Coffee-House, whose backbone had stuck out for more than nine years, yet the Tallow-Chandler of Saffron Hill issued a warning to all that she had lamed and never cured *him*, but Zounds! nobody heeded him after she did a cure on Sir Hans Sloane's Niece that became the town talk, so that Mrs. Mapp had but to show her nose in a theatre and every seat was filled by the curious who wanted to see her instead of the play, she now residing in Pall Mall though she never forgot Epsom, and gave a Plate of Ten Guineas to be run on the Race-Course, where a Mare called after herself won the first Heat in the Race, which delighted her so that she gave the Jockey a Guinea, and promised him Nine-and-Ninety more if he won the whole Race, but he failed to his mortification and that of Mrs. Mapp, who died not so very long after as poor as a Church Mouse, and was buried by the Parish of Seven Dials on December the Twenty-Second,

Seventeen-Hundred-and-Thirty-seven, a long time to be sure, yet, believe it or not, my goslings,' said the Old Grey Goose, 'you need a breath longer still to reel off this story without drawing a second, quah-quah!'

(And as sure as it's true, so will you!)

DECEMBER 23
'Holy-Month'

IT was December, meaning the Tenth Month, for the Romans; though it was sometimes called Fumosus, or Smoky, because of the fires men lit within, and sometimes Canus, or hoary, because of the rime which winter laid without.

But for the Saxons it was simply *Winter-Monath* until, in the dawn of their Christianity, they changed it to *Heligh-Monath*, or Holy-Month, because for them, as for us, it was the month of Christ's birth.

DECEMBER 24
The Princesses' Carol

ELIZABETH of Hungary
    Who wore a golden crown
Loaves for the poor ones
Carried in her gown.
Once when she went
Their hunger to fulfill
The loaves were changed to roses
By heaven's will.

Sweet Saint Elizabeth,
Let your rose light
On all young Elizabeths
Come Christmas Night.

Margaret of Scotland
Who wore a golden dress
Looked to the little ones
In loneliness.
Nine small orphans
Daily ere noon
She fed on her knees
From a porridge-spoon.

Dear Saint Margaret,
Let your love stay
By all small Margarets
Come Christmas Day.

DECEMBER 25

The Cries of Bethlehem

(*Arranged from a very old Carol*)

WHAT are the Cries of Bethlehem at Christmas on the
Night?
The shrill Cock stands on the city wall and crows:
Christus natus est!
Christus natus est!

CHRIST IS BORN!

The gobbling Ducks waddle in the mud and quack:
Quando? Quando?
Quando? Quando?

WHEN? WHEN?

The hoarse Raven flaps on the tree and croaks:
In haec nocte!
In haec nocte!

ON THIS NIGHT!

The mooing cow sways on the road and lows:
Ubi? Ubi?
Ubi? Ubi?

WHERE? WHERE?

The little Lamb peeps through the city gate and bleats:
Bethlem! Bethlem!
Bethlem! Bethlem!
Be-ee-eeth-lem . . .

IN BETHLEHEM.

These are the Cries of Bethlehem at Christmas on the Night.

DECEMBER 26

BOXING DAY

Harlequin

ON 26 December, 1717 London flocked to see the new Christmas attraction in Lincoln's-Inn-Fields:

HARLEQUIN EXECUTED
A New Italian Mimic Scene
(*never performed before*)

between a Scaramouch, a Harlequin, a Country Farmer,
his Wife, & Others.

Mr. Rich the actor, who was in low water at the time, had thought of making a hotch-potch of sparkling scenes from the old English masques and the lively farces of Harlequin and Co. from Italy. He would present his entertainment in two parts, one beautiful, one comic, and call it

The First English Pantomime!

Rich himself played Harlequin, who courted Columbine, and by the use of his magic wand amused the audience 'with a surprising variety of adventures and tricks; such as the sudden transformation of palaces and temples to huts and cottages; of men and women into wheelbarrows and joint-stools; of trees turned to houses; colonnades to beds of tulips; and mechanics' shops into serpents and ostriches.'

Pantomime became the rage; London turned out to see it again and again year after year; and Rich was the first and finest Harlequin ever seen. About a hundred years later, harlequins went down and clowns came up, when Joseph Grimaldi appeared at Covent Garden in 1807 as Gaby Grin, in 'Harlequin in his Element'. But there are not enough Riches and Grimaldis. The Harlequinade dwindled out of the fairy pageant and became a little masque at the show's tail, for old time's sake; till even the tail shrivelled up. Clown and Harlequin vanished with it; but Pantomime, sacred to Boxing Day, goes on.

DECEMBER 27
What Children Think

SOME people once wrote down things they had thought when they were children.

One thought that animals could talk; they spoke in the fairy-tales just like human beings—and in pantomimes you really *hear* them talk.

One thought the coloured Christmas-tree candles burned with coloured lights, and was sad when white and red and blue gave the same yellow flame.

One thought that sausages ran about on four little legs.

One thought that the rustling leaves on the trees made the wind.

One was surprised that other children liked their own mothers best.

One thought that lightning was a momentary glimpse into heaven.

One thought that the banks handed out money to any one who wanted it.

One thought that tears and unhappiness were things one grew out of, and was surprised to find that grown-ups can cry.

And Samuel Butler, who filled his note-books with all sorts of things, tells of a little girl he knew who asked for pencil and paper to draw with. 'But, my dear,' said her mother, 'you can't draw. If I did give you pencil and paper, how would you set about drawing?'

The little girl said, 'I should think, and then I should draw a line round my think.'

DECEMBER 28

The Dance of the Golden Trees

W HEN Henry the Eighth sat on the throne of England, a time of rich festivities set in, pageants were devised that a hundred years later developed into the enchanting masques of the Elizabethans. The idea had come to England from Florence and Venice, and pageants, to be done on Twelfth Day, were being prepared as early as December 1509. The first, to be done before the banquet in the Hall of Richmond, was

'a Pageant devised like a mountain, glistening by night as though it had been all of gold and set with stones; on the top of which mountain was a tree of gold, the branches and boughs frysed with gold, spreading on every side over the mountain with roses and pomegranates: the which mountain was with vices brought up towards the King, and out of the same came a lady apparelled in cloth of gold, and the children of honour called the henchmen, which were freshly disguised, and danced a Morris before the King, and that done, re-entered the mountain: and then was the wassail brought in.'

A century later Thomas Campion, that lovely writer of tunes and lyrics, devised a masque with music in which gold trees again appeared, and danced; the scene was

'a green valley with green trees round about it, and in the midst of them golden trees with arms and branches very glorious to behold.'

The trees were two beautiful boys—Apollo's youths—who had been enchanted by Cynthia, the Queen of the Night; but a musical incantation re-transformed them into human shape. At the first sound of the singing the trees 'began to move and dance according to the measure of the time which the musicians kept, and the nature of the words'.

The Dance of the Golden Trees! Can the sight have been lovelier, or as lovely, as the vision that moves in the mind at the sound of the words?

DECEMBER 29

Capricorn

(*A Zodiac Song*)

CAPRICORN, Capricorn
Bears December on his horn.
In the year's declining days
He has no green thing to graze.
He must drink of snow, and eat
Of ice, and men will hear him bleat
Munching at the frosty boughs
Round about the darkened house.

He will stare with agate eyes
At the empty earth and skies,
Wondering why he must bear
Scapegoat's portion of the year.
Till one night before one morn,
　　Tired and torn,
　　Patience worn,
Capricorn, Capricorn
Will toss December from his horn.

DECEMBER 30
The Old Cronies

ABOUT ten years ago a blind shoemaker lived in a village in Buckinghamshire. He was an old man, and poor, and having lost his sight he lost his work.

The shoemaker, whose name was Hawkes, was enabled at last to go to London to see what the doctors could do for him; and they did for him so well that they restored his sight. They sent him back to his village with this advice: 'Sit in the sun as much as possible.'

In his joy at seeing the sun again, Shoemaker Hawkes thought this was the very best medicine the doctors could have ordered. He took the trouble to find out where the sun shone brightest during the day; and discovered that, of all places, it shone brightest in the churchyard. So he made a habit of going daily to the place, where he sat in the sun among the grass and flowers.

Well, he wasn't the only one. You might have thought this lonely old chap would have had the churchyard to himself—but not a bit of it! In the course of the day, several other old chaps turned up, to take the sun and air there like himself. Naturally they began to chat with each other, and, meeting every day as they did, became quite a little fellowship. Then his great idea came to Shoemaker Hawkes. All these aged widowers and bachelors who met like brothers— why shouldn't they form a real fellowship, a real brotherhood? A fellowship and brotherhood of old men!

He put his idea to the other old men, and they all agreed that old men and poor need not be lonely men and sad, as long as they got together. More than a hundred of them got together, and formed The Old Men's Fellowship. None was less than seventy years old; many were over eighty; and four had topped ninety. They undertook to look after each other in their need. If one fell ill, there were ninety-nine to sit with him and nurse him. If one needed a holiday, ninety-nine put their heads together and saw that he got it. Soon a meeting-house in the village was made over to them. They used it as a club-house, where they could talk and smoke together; they used it, too, for a real meeting-house, where they held their devotional services and sang their songs with all their hearts and voices.

Met and sang, did I say? I should have said, meet and sing! And at Christmas, when they meet to celebrate, children's pipings can sound no sweeter in heaven than the cracked voices of the old cronies, this jolly Fellowship of the Aged, who refuse to be lonely because they are old, and sad because they are poor.

The Old Cronies

Meredith. W. Hawes.

DECEMBER 31

Up the Hill, down the Hill

OLD One, lie down,
   Your journey is done,
Little New Year
Will rise with the sun.
Now you have come to
The foot of the hill,
Lay down your bones,
Old Year, and lie still.

Young One, step out,
Your journey's begun,
Weary Old Year
Makes way for his son.
Now you have started
To climb up the hill,
Put best foot forward,
New Year, with a will.

   Up the hill, down the hill,
   Which is the best?
   Up-hill is labour,
   And down-hill is rest.